A
Harlequin
Romance

OTHER

Harlequin Romances

by MARGARET WAY

Many of these titles are available at your local bookseller
or through the Harlequin Reader Service.

For a free catalogue listing all available Harlequin Romances,
send your name and address to:

HARLEQUIN READER SERVICE,
M.P.O. Box 707, Niagara Falls, N.Y. 14302
Canadian address: Stratford, Ontario, Canada.

or use order coupon at back of book.

REEDS OF HONEY

by

MARGARET WAY

HARLEQUIN BOOKS   TORONTO WINNIPEG

Original hard cover edition published in 1975
by Mills & Boon Limited.

© Margaret Way 1975

SBN 373-01889-4

Harlequin edition published July 1975

*All the characters in this book have no existence outside the
imagination of the Author, and have no relation whatsoever to
anyone bearing the same name or names. They are not even
distantly inspired by any individual known or unknown to the
Author, and all the incidents are pure invention.*

The H a r l e q u i n trade mark, consisting of the word
HARLEQUIN and the portrayal of a Harlequin, is registered
in the United States Patent Office and in the Canada Trade
Marks Office.

In 300 B.C., on an expedition to India, one Nearchus, admiral to Alexander the Great, reported that he had seen 'reeds that produced honey although there were no bees'. This was the earliest known reference to sugar-cane growing.

In 1817 the first sugar cane, introduced from the Society Islands, was grown on the Australian mainland. Today, Australia is one of the largest producers of sugar in the world, leading the way in the mechanical cultivation and harvesting of the crop.

CHAPTER ONE

IT was one of those soft, flawless days when the sea and the sky seemed to meet. A world of exquisite blueness, such luminous serenity it invaded the mind. Frances lay back, as graceful as a cat in her cushioned rattan chair with its high, curving back. She felt marvellously at peace, caught up in this enchanting world of sunshine. The blue and the gold—a summer idyll. It was a curiously sensuous feeling to be flooded with bright heat, yet the breeze was like silk on her cheeks, ruffling the thick, massy swing of hair like polished rosewood. She gave the softest little sigh of pleasure and abandonment. On such a supremely lovely day she should have been able to think great thoughts, but they simply wouldn't come. It was enough just to *be*, with sensations like honey bees buzzing in and out of her head. Probably the whole city felt the same way, for no one could be immune to the great pull of nature at her most beautiful and benign, shimmering, spilling, exploding around them.

The sun porch was a cool, greeny-gold grotto, catching the bright reflection of the terrace and beyond, a sweeping view of the Harbour, the blue sparkling Waitamata. At this time on Saturday morning, the traffic was streaming along the motorway that lay at the foot of their sandstone cliff frontage, and on to the Bridge. The Bridge was a familiar sight. It very nearly sprang from the bottom of their garden where only a decade and a half ago the blue bay had lapped, silvering the sands, beckoning to those in the house to come down for a swim. The matchless pleasure of racing down the garden slopes, diving in, swimming furiously, arms flailing the crystal-clear water, turning over, floating lazily, with the blue sea swirling and swelling, the splashing and the laughter.... But there had been compensations. Now their view set them apart a little from everyone else. The fascination of perpetual motion; of life and movement with the Bridge, by day, an efficient metallic diadem linking the green parkland of Point Erin with the beautiful marine suburbs of the North Shore; by night, with the flick of a switch, lit to enchantment with the companion lights of Westhaven, a model boat basin.

If she shifted her head slightly, Frances could see, there beyond the glowing scarlet line of the blossoming Pohutakawas, Rangitoto rise sheer out of the sea in its wonderful cone-shaped symmetry, proclaiming for all, world traveller and New Zealander alike, the city's identity: this is Auckland, sapphire of the South Seas. Frances let her eyes linger on the volcano's blue into grape into violet-shrouded lava slopes. One had to be a lot closer to see the outlying scoria reefs. It was Rangitoto, she considered, even more than its profoundly beautiful sea-cradled shores, that lent Auckland its unique flavour. Rangitoto was somehow real, not just a splendid natural phenomenon, superbly sited to dominate the Harbour's inner entrance, Rangitoto was a beloved figure, more like some legendary Maori chieftain, simply and effortlessly majestic. To vulcanologists, it might pose an awesome question, extinct some twinkling eight hundred years, like a giant only lightly asleep; to Frances, Rangitoto spelled all that was New Zealand, all that she had come to know and love. A monument, a monumental love. Some people, and she was one of them, were gripped by nature in all its moods, held in its giant leafy hands so it became a kind of obsession. Such things started in childhood, the call and the response to nature's siren song so that now she was steeped in it like some mystical experience.

From early this morning, from every bay, every inlet, every private mooring, the sails of the Waitamata had slipped out, skimming the shimmering, silver-flecked foam, a regatta in honour of summer with the gulls wheeling and shrieking overhead in disorganised, joyous formation. Under the Bridge and beyond the breakwater, past the yacht clubhouses, the big, white-sailed sloops had already slipped away for the island retreats of the Hauraki Gulf, Motutapu, Motuihi, Rakino, Waiheke, and beyond them in the jacaranda-blue distance, Kawau as beautiful as a dream. Just to sound their names conjured up visions of romance and she had memories of all of them.

But here, in the present, she could sink back blissfully in her chair, the sun flashing out all the rose ambers in her velvety head. Her far-away, dreaming, wide-open eyes were the colour of amber, black-fringed in a small, distinctly elegant face, tanned at this time of the year to a pale, even gold, like the slender young limbs coiled with such languid cat-grace. If she was slightly under average height, a sore point because she admired tall, willowy figures, the perfect clothes-horses, Frances was beautifully balanced from long years of ballet lessons and a Solo Seal Diploma from the Royal

Academy—her one major accomplishment, though she could swim like a fish and little excuse if she couldn't. She could handle a boat and a car, and draw more than well, which had earned her her scholarship to the Technical College in the first place. When she finished her training she hoped to become a textile designer and she had already turned out some excellent designs for silk screen which she looked like being paid for. All in all, she appeared to be justifying the long years of single-minded planning and devotion that her mother had expended on her only child. At any rate, a wonderful bond of love and compatibility existed between them so that even the thought of one for the other made eyes and voice and expression soften.

Right at that moment, from their gleaming, super-efficient kitchen, came the comforting associated small sounds of her mother preparing a delicious brunch for them both. Soon the aromas would follow. Frances didn't have to be in the kitchen to have a clear picture of her mother, dark-haired, dark-eyed, amazingly youthful and attractive, navy flares and a chic striped jersey sweater, a faint frown hazing the softness of her expression as she applied her considerable culinary powers to the job at hand. Rae Campbell adored cooking and baking and preserving and all the things Frances couldn't, except cleaning up afterwards, which her mother quite fairly refused to do.

Surprisingly, in view of these Cordon Bleu feats, both of them had enviably slim figures, but a great deal of the cooking was given over to the business-cum-pleasure-cum-overseas visitors type of thing, the non-stop entertaining expected of the family of a prominent business man and leading yachtsman.

This weekend promised to be blissfully lazy with Chris away on a short trip to Australia. Not that Frances didn't love her stepfather. She did, and admired him enormously, but it was lovely to be on their own very occasionally without the dynamo that was Chris Campbell; the swarming attendant sea of friendly faces that invariably surrounded him, necessitating the impromptu, never-ending 'You will have a cup of coffee?' Chris *was* hospitality, and Frances did make excellent coffee, the single creative activity she was allowed in the kitchen where her mother reigned supreme, a true artist, great as a performer, with diminishing teaching powers. Frances didn't worry. She had the uncaring confidence of the young that it would all come to her in a flash like some legendary green finger handed down through the female line.

Not that one actually needed a green finger in New Zealand. Nature took the work out of everything when flowers and trees, the wonderful tree ferns rioted in profusion, where every mile was lined with the silver sentinel spears of the toitoi grass, the sword leaves of flax with its distinctively ornamental flowers; or hydrangeas gone wild and the blue and white agapanthus, stands of the picturesque cabbage trees, the blossoming tea trees and mile upon mile of golden gorse. New Zealand was a magic place; a scenic wonderland of remarkable diversity from the blue tranquillity of the Northland to the unsurpassed grandeur of the Southern Alps. She was hopelessly in love with it, yet she wasn't a New Zealander at all. A first cousin, perhaps. An Australian, an exile from her own country as her father had been. Not that she could remember very much about her father, for all her marked resemblance to the photograph on her dressing table.

Her father had been killed in a senseless, needless accident, a type of suicide really, trying to ride a notoriously rogue horse. It had thrown him, not easily, but twice as viciously, lashing out at its unseated rider in a fine rage. The first kick would have been enough. And this tragedy less than a year after Rob Donovan had stormed away from his own father's house and the family's multiple business interests, with the expectation of never receiving 'a threepenny bit' ringing in his ears. All that time ago when Frances had been barely six, her mother, too generous-natured to be bitter, had packed up and sought sanctuary in hospitable New Zealand, throwing the deep trough of the Tasman between herself and her father-in-law. A man whose rule over his family, the small country town where he lived, his various business interests, had been complete. Neither of his two sons, who worked tirelessly for their father, had active control over anything. It was, and always would be Old Man Donovan around whom the whole structure of power would revolve.

Rae Donovan, as she had been then, abdicated immediately, too independent to have her life and the life of her child swallowed up by the Old Man. Even then Frances, an auburn-haired moppet, with a sweet, prickly streak, had been her grandfather's one tender spot, but her mother had foreseen that it would only be a matter of time before Frances, too, rebelled against such iron authority. Frances had a lot of her father in her, and neither of them had that colouring for nothing. If the flame and the temperament that lit it was a direct legacy from the Old Man himself, everyone chose to forget it. Rob Donovan and his daughter had entirely missed

12

the ruthless streak, substituting in varying degrees a gay recklessness instead. It was the vivid impulsiveness in her daughter that occasionally opened up old wounds for Rae.

Frances would need a firm hand from the one, important, man in her life, but up to date she had shown little interest in the dominant male, preferring in her ever-changing wide circle of admirers the capacity to allow themselves to be eclipsed and even led by that charmingly determined and sometimes wilful young woman. Perversely they seemed not to mind her every last little act of capriciousness, and at least one of the circle downright worshipped her. One either had charm or one hadn't, and those lucky enough to possess it seemed able to pull off anything short of murder.

Rae Campbell, wheeling the trolley through from the kitchen, viewed her daughter's carelessly elegant young body with deep maternal pride and affection. Fran's bright colouring, not her own, made enormous appeal to her artistic streak. Beautiful, she thought, the sun skipping like sequins along that dark flame head, glossing the slender, finely made limbs that emerged from a brief yellow halter-necked sundress, one of several Rae herself had run up in one afternoon. Above the luminous reflection of yellow rose a small, very elegant cat-face. Triangular. Wide cheekbones, pointed chin. The shattering, amber clarity of eyes that were faintly set at a slant. A wide, lovely mouth that was always on the brink of a smile or a quick answer. In total, a quicksilver quality. Rob. Rob's face. Rob's daughter. For a moment memory worked strongly in her so that she halted in her tracks. One never let go of the past. Never. It lived on for ever in the senses, like the sight of hair that lit up like ribbons

13

of flame. . . . She was a young girl again and more than twenty years of her life fell away like the walls of this house she had found refuge in . . .

She was at her first dance. A noisy, colourful affair. A country dance. Bright dresses and bright faces, the high, sweet, *nervous* voices of the girls. The drawly, laughing voices, deep and confident of the men. She could hear the music and the *voices* so clearly. Distinctive, Australian, not the more precisely considered voices she had become used to. Then, a young man. Tall, wide-shouldered, not much more than a boy. Rather haughty, and she found out why. Dark marmalade hair, a neat, chiselled face, hollow cheeked, clear amber eyes, faintly slanting, a lazy beguiling voice much better brought up than the rest. Robert Donovan. Rob. Old Man Donovan's son and he had been *Old Man Donovan* then when he couldn't have been much more than Rae's age now. Living made one realise how young forty was. The rest was all lost in the hammering of her heart. She had fallen in love that night and she had never fallen out of it. A woman never forgot her first love and Rob had been that. Her husband too, and the over-anxious father of a healthy, squawling, scarlet-faced, hour-old mite she had wanted to call Roberta because the resemblance even then had been so laughable, and so heart-stopping and so wonderful. In the end, their one perfect creation had been called Frances, after her own dear mother. It had been a living purgatory trying to forget Rob, but she had to in order to survive and be mother and father to her small child. Her real youth, the fine careless rapture, had died with Rob, but she had learnt to forget—an hour, a day, then weeks at a time. Later Chris had come along and made her strong again. She had come to maturity with Chris and the years had been good, but she could trace all that was Rob in his daughter.

From a nymph absolutely abandoned to the beauty in front of her Frances suddenly turned and smiled at her mother, and Frances smiling was irresistible. Rae felt an indescribable surge of happiness. It came for her, rushing like a torrent, pushing down the walls of old memories, setting her on course again. Having a lovely, loving daughter was better than having a million dollars. Chris loved Frances too, and for that alone Rae sometimes thought she would have married him. Very few people ever bothered to remember that she had been a tragic young widow with a small child when she had first come to New Zealand. It was Chris who had brought peace and stability into their lives, direction and reason for living, a heart big enough to easily encompass another man's child. Frances had been reared exactly as if she had been his own. To please him she had made the decision to change her name to his own. They were a family, very much so. They were lucky indeed.

'You're looking at me as if I were a fairy child!' Frances uncoiled herself swiftly and went to wheel the trolley the last few feet into the room.

'You are!' Her mother smiled at her, and automatically began to recheck the loaded wagon. Cool melon balls, lemon flavoured with a sprig of mint ... Frances always liked fruit with her breakfast. Sometimes she only had a piece of fruit with a cup of coffee, but the weekends were different. Piping hot ham-filled omelettes garnished with button mushrooms and freshly chopped parsley. Small, crusty rolls warm from the oven, lots of creamy butter balls, a jug of cream and plenty of coffee, newly ground and brewed to perfection. Even their American guests praised Rae's coffee, which was really saying something. The most deliciously insistent morning call of them all, Frances always said, her head under the sheets. Now she was placing the lime green linen mats and napkins, dark green into black Mikasa oven-to-table ware with a lime green scroll centre plate and a lime ring around the tall cups. The visual impression was so important, like the African violets in the centre of the table in their lovely pottery bowl.

Frances sighed her enthusiasm. 'Why is it that on the rare occasions I've ever been allowed to cook omelettes they never turn out like this?'

'You use the wrong pan, darling,' her mother murmured in rather a half-hearted fashion. 'One must treat one's omelette pan with great respect.'

'Well, if you will hide it!' Frances retaliated.

'Then you'll just have to find your own. Remember if you insist on using the big frying pan with only two eggs in it, you'll get a very dry, papery layer. With reasonable care, a good omelette is child's play.'

'All right, I surrender. It's silly to expect so much of myself anyway. Isn't it a perfect day? A serene vision. I've already flipped it away to pull out on a rainy day.'

'Poetry, sheer poetry,' her mother seconded, still in that curious offhand way, so that Frances looked at her hard—a searching look that told her her mother wasn't her usual carefree self. In fact, her face in its cloud of dark brown hair looked unwontedly sober.

'What is it? What's up?' she demanded.

'I'm not as transparent as all that, surely?'

'You certainly are!'

'Well, let's have a bite to eat first. I've so been looking forward to this.'

'You were perfectly all right ten minutes ago,' Frances persisted. 'How so?'

'Mail. A letter, from your Grandfather Donovan,' Rae said, enunciating with the utmost precision a name that had always upset her.

'My dear, is that possible?' Frances gripped her arm. 'Kindly old Pops Donovan?'

Her mother murmured something quite intelligible and Frances, for once, stared blankly out the window. 'Well, that does it! After how many years?'

'You weren't quite six when we left and I'm still reeling from your twenty-first. Nevertheless, it's interesting. I can't pretend I'm not put out I wasn't invited, but if I were you, darling, I'd go.'

'You know darn well you'd never go. Go where, anyway? Not Queensland. Sugar Hill?'

'Where your grandfather is the lord of creation. Yes, my darling.'

'Well, let it lie there and talk about something else. This omelette is as good as it looks.'

'Won't you be guided by a cooler, wiser head?'

'What a silly question!' Frances said calmly. 'Mother, I don't understand you at all. Surely the whole thing is ridiculous. Am I going to see the letter?'

'No!' her mother said pleasantly. 'It's addressed to me and contains certain little snippets which might cause you a certain amount of indignation, fiery little thing that you are, for ever flying to your mother's defence. Your grandfather is really a very fine man. Ruthless, of course, very ruthless. Still, it's possible he's mellowed. We all do, in time.' Casually she broke a roll in half and raised a piece to her mouth, all the while avoiding her daughter's eye.

'That heartless old man!' Frances said in a very strong tone, static forming about her as if she might catch fire so that her mother, betrayed into glancing into that silky young face, burst into laughter.

'Honestly, darling, you wouldn't back off from the devil! I'm not sure if that's good or not, but it's the way you are. I'm only telling you your grandfather has written inviting you to spend the summer vacation with him and the rest of the happy gang. I have to admit he has in the past caused more than his fair share of unpleasantness, but he sounds lonely. A lonely old man—you could very well brighten his life. He's quite staggeringly financial—not that he could ever be persuaded to part with much.'

'*You'd* never have taken it at any rate. From all I can piece together for myself, because you never will talk about it, my dear old Grandfather Donovan treated my father very badly, so why should I go, and why should you want me to go?'

Her mother looked back at her with her humorous brown eyes. 'Perhaps he's learnt a hard lesson, or at least how to behave himself!'

'We don't know that for certain. You've said so yourself, and I distinctly remember, Grandfather Donovan has a motive for everything. Method in his madness and so forth.'

'I wonder!' Rae Campbell fell silent for a moment, seemingly looking into her mind's eye. 'Anyway, he's an old man now, darling. It's not my nature nor yours to be ungenerous. You're his grandchild, after all. He may well wish to make amends for past injustices, and as I say, he's splendidly rich. As I recall, he owned the whole town as well as one of the most prosperous sugar farms in the whole North.'

'Well, that's not influencing me any!' Gratefully Frances held up her coffee cup. 'I should miss all this dreadfully. I can't go.'

'You're weakening, and no wonder! You're insatiably curious—you always were even as a small child, and they're your own people after all. It's my duty to encourage you to spread your wings, then Chris and I could go off cruising without worrying about you here in the house on your own.'

'I like that!'

'You know what I mean, Fran. North Queensland is something else again—the tropics, brilliantly flamboyant, quite different!'

'I remember!' Frances said oddly. 'Word of a Donovan!' And she *could* remember, not the people so much but the place, the heat and the long wriggling snakes. No snakes in New Zealand, but plenty along the rich red tracks that cut through the green cane that stood as tall as a man. She could remember the crackling barbaric splendour of the firing, frighteningly exciting to a small child. The black smoke and the flame and there in the soft New Zealand sunshine—she shivered remembering. And the storms! With the taut sky brilliant with lightning, monsoonal storms that blew in from the ocean bringing seething life to the soil. The poinciana trees—she could remember them clearly, enormous crimson arches. The great mango trees heavy with fruit, and climbing over everything, the bougainvillea, thorny and defying all attempts to cut it back, but beautiful with its lush display of crimson and rose and white. And the rain! And the start of the Wet and wallowing in mud. She had a clear recollection of tall yellow gumboots. Now wasn't that odd? Unconsciously Frances shook back her head and her amber eyes sparkled as if under some powerful fascination.

'Frances?'

She turned her head quickly and caught the lingering expression on her mother's face, faintly sad. 'Now why look like that?' she said without hesitation, puzzled on her own account.

'Perhaps it was the "word of a Donovan" that did it. After all these years of being Frances Campbell, you suddenly come out with "word of a Donovan" and to my certain knowledge you've never said it before.'

'I just made it up that very minute,' Frances smiled. 'Honestly, I can't even remember saying it.'

'Your father used to say it all the time,' Rae said quietly, with a reminiscent little sigh. 'Which proves beyond all question that we live again in our children, something always kept and handed down to the next generation, gifts and defects. There *is* no release from the past.'

'Oh, cheer up, darling,' Frances said swiftly, possessed by the unhappy notion that her mother was about to cry. 'You know as well as I do I'm a daughter in a million, beautiful, charming, intelligent. You've said so yourself, many times. Anyone would think you had a little horror on your hands! It's that letter, it's upset you—and no wonder! I'm going to take it from you by force and reply to it if needs be.'

'You'll never find it. I've hidden it. . . .'

'Along with the omelette pan. On such a perfect day to have a wind from Hell blow in!'

'My dearest child, whatever are you talking

about? Don't let our mood of the morning slip away from us. If I was upset for a tiny moment forget about it. It's not always possible to control our most deeply felt emotions. I loved your father very much. You're very much like him, at different times almost a mirror image. I mean everything, looks and manner. This letter out of the blue ... well, I don't really know what to make of it.'

'He's up to some kind of mischief, I can see that.'

'No mischief, darling. Your grandfather always loved you. You were the apple of his eye.'

'He very conveniently forgot that!'

Rae Campbell set her cup down hard. She was a fair woman and she had always felt an uncomfortable stab about her former father-in-law, but she had done what she thought best at the time. He was an old tyrant and he positively demanded unswerving allegiance, but it must have been a great wrench for him losing sight of his little granddaughter, the one person ever game to dictate to him. A picture focused of Frances and the Old Man, Frances chattering about everything, piercing that strange, hard shell Vincent Donovan always wore about him. Whatever had they talked about—and they had talked all the time? He had treated her as a princess, certainly, but a small friend, his only friend. He had never shown the same loving indulgence to his two sons and explosive Rob had stormed out in a climax of bitter arguments. There had been little preparation for the Old Man. He had obviously never anticipated nor taken into account his own son's temperament. Rob had worked hard and long because he loved 'his old man', but it wasn't until Rob was dead that they all realised how much that love was returned, but inwardly, silently, dismissing with scorn any visible demonstrations.

After Rob's death, the Old Man had got harder and harder and Rae had packed up and gone away rejecting all that was Vincent Donovan and in turn being rejected. No one turned their back on the Old Man, and she had done just that. Now in this lovely long summer the past had come back. She didn't quite know why she wanted Frances to go back, for a time, but she did. Retribution perhaps, but for what? The penalties one paid through life. Then Frances, out of nowhere, says 'word of a Donovan', with that teasing, audacious tilt to her head. The pampered, adopted daughter of Chris Campbell had changed the pattern of her life in a minute.

She *was* Frances Donovan, of course—that was it. One could grow up anywhere, against any background, and still revert in an instant to the call of blood. Something basic in the psychology, physiology, whatever. Rae crossed her arms in front of her in a self-protective fashion, more unsettled than she knew. The letter had distressed her and annoyed her too. The Old Man had a genius for the odd, trenchant remark, always putting the other person in the wrong, but one thing had emerged clearly. He wanted to see his granddaughter. Vincent Donovan, who found it almost impossible to tell anyone anything, had plainly told her it would give him great pleasure to see 'young Fran' again. He had been ill—not a bid for sympathy, because he wasn't like that. If Vincent Donovan said he was ill, he *was* ill. Her attitude would be important and he was relying on her not to influence the girl against him. He could at least be fair. What was love anyway? Was she the only person who knew how to love, or deserved to love?

22

It was hard for the Old Man, being how he was, and harder for him still to write.

Frances, across the table, let her eyes dwell on her mother for these interminable minutes. Her coffee had gone cold, but no matter. Her mother had only pecked at what was in front of her. So much for this blissful morning together. Just like old Pops Donovan to announce himself in this fashion, yet why did she feel this undercurrent of excitement? A lick of warmth along her veins, not gentle heat ... *flame!*

'This is ridiculous!' she heard herself saying. 'I'm beginning to think there's no positive stand on anything. Do you mean to tell your innocent only daughter life is a series of ambiguities with half a dozen different answers to a given question? I thought we came to New Zealand to escape Grandfather. Why, you threw the whole moat of the Tasman between us, and now when we get one of his outrageous letters we fall apart like a pair of sentimentalists, dead set on placating him. Why, it's *reedeeculous!*' she exclaimed, drawing the words out. 'I mean, an annual visit is one thing, but this is quite shocking!'

'Maybe shocks make us see things a lot quicker!' said her mother. 'According to his lights, your grandfather never rejected us. It was the other way around and he was always very proud and stubborn. I can't think now that *I* did the wrong thing. By the same token I can't keep repeating old mistakes. The letter read like a "forgive me" in as much as the Old Man could ever say such a thing. It dissolves old resentments—not that I ever felt any. I was fortunate in that way. Some people nurse the old grievances for a lifetime. The funny part is you could never see enough of your grandfather when

23

you were a child. Poppy—what a name! Your father always thought it the most unsuitable name in the world for the Old Man.'

'Strange,' mused Frances, 'I've forgotten him, yet I remember Sugar Hill.'

'Stranger still, we hear you sound so exactly someone else!' Rae said with an odd look of triumph and sadness. 'After your father was killed, I never felt so alone in my life, surrounded by people. As if I'd always be alone and wanted it that way in my misery. But life starts again. We can't stand still for anyone or anything. I had you. I could never go back, though, to Sugar Hill. Too much love, too many bitter arguments and things that went wrong. I can't begin to understand why, but I'd like you to go. If you want to, and only then.'

'Goodness, to think I started off so cheerful! You know,' Frances sighed, 'I'm allergic to all this soul-searching. Why don't we let Chris decide? Just to see him might calm us. I fancy Grandfather likes creating ripples. *You* didn't come out unscathed. Neither did Father. For all we know I might be putting my sweet little head in the lion's den. It's not as if he's a gentle, nice man, the old warhorse!'

'You're somewhat fiery yourself, but miraculously good-tempered otherwise!'

There was a mutually affectionate pause while Frances got up to pour fresh coffee for them both. 'Let's shelve it for a while,' she said in a pleasant, accommodating tone. 'I mean I suppose I really can't go on saying the most unforgivable things about my own grandfather. When Chris comes home we'll thrash out this little problem, and not before then. Today I intend to get drunk on salt air and sea and sunshine. Why, it's not as if I *want* to go! North Queensland—heavens, this time of year I should melt!'

'That's one of the most curious things about you, darling!' her mother said, smiling. 'For all your red hair, you *don't*. You have a natural affinity for the sun—and there are hats, you know!'

'Hats, yes!' Frances twirled to face the big oval mirror, her amber eyes glowing, conveying an inner vision of herself, Scarlett O'Hara fashion. She laughed and her mother laughed too, but neither of them really knew what they were laughing about. Only one thing was really apparent— Frances had come to the point of not going back, like waking very early with no way of getting back to sleep, something recognised and accepted. For better or worse she would spend this long, luxurious summer in her grandfather's house, the house where she had been born. Back, in effect, to mark one and the grandfather she had clung to like a bright flower, a fantastically pretty child he had called 'my little Fran'.

Perhaps after all, Rae thought wryly, there was a real pattern to everything and life wasn't some haphazard, abstract tapestry woven of love and anger, laughter and empty silences and inevitable tragedy. Perhaps this was the time set aside for reconciliation. If they bypassed this opportunity it would come again not at all. Frances would never need anyone to make her decisions. She wasn't even one of those people who needed the necessary backing to move. The decision had already been made and it gleamed out of eyes sparkling with old infatuations. Frances was, without question, going to Sugar Hill where she would be known and accepted as Frances Donovan, heiress to the Old Man.

CHAPTER TWO

FROM the first moment Frances set foot on Queensland soil, she was reborn, reclaimed by a country to which she really belonged—a country as vivid and vital as herself, but she had never fully realised this. All she knew was, from the very first sight of the house where she had been born, the skin on her nape began to prickle and all the little qualms she had about herself settled. She was home, but it took her a long time to admit this, torn as she was by her love and loyalty for the country of her adoption.

Her grandfather was an aristocrat, not an old warhorse at all but a lion, not to be trifled with, and anyone with half an eye would see this at once. The stern, fine features were still hard and purposeful, the shrewd, unblinking, amber eyes only lightening for a slip of a girl. His granddaughter, Frances. The old, strangely sweet affinity was working, one of those inexplicable things no one can explain save as an indestructible blood link. Then, too, Vincent Donovan was fantastic—rich enough with more than enough presence for ordinary, hardworking people to think it only reasonable he should ride about and greet his long-lost granddaughter in a chauffeur-driven Rolls-Royce, the incomparable Silver Ghost he had imported in the early 1920s. So much care and attention had been lavished upon it, fifty years later, it might just as easily have only rolled off the production line. The finest motor car in the world, said Vincent Donovan, and Frances was drawn to it with equal attraction.

She was home, to her grandfather's world—a powerful, faintly primitive world full of unexplored exotica with the rains to come, the life-giving monsoons and sometimes the harbingers of death and destruction when every river, every lake, every lone waterhole and billabong joined forces to run together in a torrent across the endless plains. Flood, cyclones, disaster. But not now, not in this unexplored December with only some hazy dreams of her early childhood to guide her. Frances recognised the implacable quality in her grandfather, but she could refuse him nothing in these days of reunion. He was old, very old, and soon he might leave the earth in one mighty bound like the majestic old lion he resembled.

Frances had exchanged one way of life for another and it seemed to her both fitting and right, for in her grandfather's eyes she saw herself faithfully mirrored, with love. She was strong enough and generous enough to yield part of herself to this strange, hard man, enigmatic and remote, yet fiery and hot-tempered on occasion; a man who all his long life had only truly loved one person—herself. Perhaps she alone of all of them accepted him unquestioningly, asking nothing, temperamentally in tune with a child's tenderness. Whatever the reason, she alone had broken through Vincent Donovan's iron-hard barriers. He would have granted her anything, and all the old questions were better left unspoken. Nothing must disturb this visit or her grandfather's last days. So Frances looked about her with questing, eager eyes, and the more she looked, the more she saw and remembered.

The house—Sugar Hill, a huge white rambling building that had once been magnificent, a fine example of Queensland Colonial with its wide, deeply shaded verandas, surrendering its civilised stand to the ravenous demands of the tropical wilderness that all but smothered its grounds and stopped short of its four broad timber steps. It might have been a rain forest or a tropical Eden, complete with snakes, a bewildering welter of swiftly blossoming and equally swiftly decaying vegetation, so prolific, so densely thick and green, it was a kind of no-man's land, off limits to any sensible tourist. Clearly any form of gardening or imposing restraint on magnificent nature had been given up as a dying occupation. Almost Frances expected to see a crocodile struggle out of the dead flat, darkly green natural lake, that now resembled a swamp, but lavish with the most exquisite waxy perfection of the ivory and hyacinth lotus lilies that flowered so prolifically in the humid heat.

And the bats that shrieked and flapped about at night! And the birds, by day, gorgeous lorikeets, and small, furry creatures that fed off the fruits of the giant mango trees, the figs, the bananas, pawpaws and avocadoes. It was all incredibly lush, yet exuberant too, and Frances marked within herself the contrast to the graceful rather melancholy beauty of the New Zealand bush, more a matter of line—the lovely, down-curving fronds of the New Zealand native pongas, the tree ferns, and the soaring, shaftlike, light leafiness of the Australian eucalypt. Chris had once called his own bush 'sad' and she could see now what he meant. All this prodigally flowering bush about her was essentially 'open', happy, if one liked, for all its hectic blossoming and always above them, the intensely blue sky, a brilliant, cloudless cobalt, a white-hot dazzle of sunshine, and it got to her.

By the end of the first day she had all but mastered her fear and repulsion of the snakes and the truly hideous cane toads and ventured beyond the broad avenue of large, symmetrically shaped hoop pines that lined the straight drive to the front gate. In this jungle of the grounds there were the innumerable lillypillies that so drew the birds, the red and white cedars and the flame trees with their peculiarly flattened buttresses, the giant figs festooned with native orchids, the carabeens, the peppermints, the stringy barks and the ironwoods, the beautiful rose gums with their aromatic crushed leaves. Only an expert could have identified the wealth of trees or indeed beaten a track through the sea of tangled vines.

It was nature on the grand scale and Frances found herself revelling in it—the tropics on the verge of the wet when everything burst into flamboyant blooms, the magnificent poincianas and the West African tulips that broke open their scarlet blossom, the treelike banks of frangipanni with its marvellous, heady perfume, the rampant golden trumpets of the allamanda and the brilliantly aggressive bougainvillea that threatened to pull down a great mango and climbed up one side of the house and spilled half way across the roof. Yet somehow the house emerged victorious, and halting within a quarter mile of the front door were the luminous, indescribably emerald canefields, like a giant salad bowl encircling the house, springing so quickly to maturity in the rich red volcanic soil. Sugar Hill itself was set on high ground, very likely the crater of some primeval volcano that still made the soil seethe. The violent, beautiful earth. It was all much more fantastic than she could have remembered or imagined, and it was quite irresistible, commanding her respect yet demanding her attention.

Though Frances looked like a tiger lily, she was, in fact, a worker, and there was a great deal to be done. The homestead was almost an echo of itself and a curious challenge like a beautiful woman going right out of her way to make herself unattractive and never succeeding. But after all, in spite of her enthusiasm, it wasn't her problem. There was Rosa, her aunt by marriage, her Uncle Desmond's widow, and Dario, her son, a Donovan and never a Donovan, for he was entirely his mother, a black-eyed, raven-haired, picturesquely good-looking Italian. A happy, lighthearted extrovert son; an implacable, ambitious goddess of a mother. The stuff of drama—and Frances was yet to find what part she played in it.

Certainly Rosa had greeted the new arrival guardedly, reserving warmth and judgment, but scrupulously, urbanely polite. Rosa, a heavily handsome woman with a superb olive skin, definite classic features and a wealth of lustrous black hair drawn back into a gleaming intricate knot. Rosa had long since determined never to forsake her father-in-law's house. There was Dario to consider. He was a big disappointment to the Old Man and this was a bitter thorn of resentment in her maternal breast. Dario alone would have kept her bound to the Old Man. Dario, in time, would become a very wealthy man and she as his mother, and moreover an Italian mother, to be cherished and obeyed for a lifetime, would naturally benefit. A quiet luxury suited her. At some time in the near future she and Dario would be free to follow their own desires. Dario was no farmer but an artist, at war with his environment—not in its physical aspects, for he had already committed to canvas the multiple beauties of the North, but rather the whole idea of conformity to his grandfather's ideas and ideology. The concept of what was suitable for a Donovan. And worst of all, work! The need to work, work, work, if one was to succeed. The management and the supervision, and the necessary physical labour —and Dario was a splendidly fit young man, but it was apparent even to his adoring mother that he rejected the whole principle of the dignity of labour. Neither was he unhappy nor frustrated, for he was basically lazy, but Rosa considered, given a dedicated and determined mother, she could drive him along to make a name for himself. In Italy, perhaps, for Rosa vividly remembered the eternal city of her birth. Rosa, something of an enigma herself.

The immigrant Italian families and their descendants, as she frequently reminded everyone, had opened up the North. North Queensland, she meant, which indeed owed and admitted a great debt to its Italian population for settling the North and contributing so largely to the prosperity and importance of the sugar industry. If it was not obvious nor even thought of by Frances, it was apparent to Rosa, who had come to understand the Old Man's mind and its workings, that Frances had been introduced into this far from happy home in order to bring to it new life and order, a continuity of family. Family. *Family*. For all his faults, and Rosa considered her father-in-law to be an arrogant and opinionated old man, Vincent Donovan had a great passion for family continuity.

A Donovan to inherit the land. Work it and grow rich from it. Powerful too. Dario, alone, could never accomplish this. Dario, whom his grandfather called Desmond, was in fact hopelessly miscast as a man of property and certainly no business man. His interests were few—pretty girls, good food, good wine, a fast car, a soft bed to sleep in, plenty of nice clothes—and when the impulse gripped him, not always at a convenient time, the need to paint. It was more a compulsion that mastered him despite himself. His talent, and it was undeniable, had come, oddly enough, with his Donovan blood. Both the Old Man's sons, his own father and the tragic young Robert, had been gifted with an exceptional facility—witness the innumerable sketchbooks of Dario's father, Desmond. Those superb horses, the wild bush horses, stock horses, ponies and thoroughbreds; bright, fiery eyes, slender, powerful legs and flashing manes. Desmond's brother, Robert, had been killed outright by a flying hoof—a rogue horse. The terrible irony of life.

Now Robert's daughter, 'Fran' to the Old Man, flitted though the rambling old house like a bright vision, with her grandfather a born dictator, putty in her delicate hands—another terrible irony. Dario was his grandchild as well, though it might have been better for him had he inherited the Donovan red hair. Only occasionally did Rosa, his mother, think this, for she greatly preferred the volatile dark vitality of her son's Italian ancestry. The Old Man's obsession with family had brought the girl here and she could not be condemned. She was a striking-looking girl and had made an instant and immediate appeal to her cousin Dario, who worshipped more than anything a woman's beauty, and Frances was so disturbingly lovely and friendly too, very warm and outgoing. Within a week Dario was completely infatuated, while his mother subjected the girl to a merciless assessment, thinking her own thoughts, as fathomless as a piece of medieval sculpture.

Frances, in her turn, accepted all this silent scrutiny with a bland calm. She was enjoying herself far too much to even consider whether her grandfather might be up to all the old machinations, even if he sincerely believed his plan to be in the best interests of the family. Now that Frances had returned to his house he intended to keep her there. She was the light of his life, as receptive to him as a young woman as she had ever been as a child, and unlike most women, for whom he had not a great deal of time, she tried neither to probe nor disturb their inbuilt affinity or resurrect all the old griefs. Such things were unchangeable. Few people went through life without at least one major cyclone. The winds blew and one weathered them or went under.

For once Dario was granted a full reprieve from work with his grandfather's blessing. It was the most welcome challenge in the world to show his beautiful cousin the beautiful surrounding countryside. and this with the greatest good humour and a natural wooing manner. In no way did he make Frances feel a kind of 'would-be if she could' usurper, as Rosa managed without words at all. Streaking past the long line of canefields, her hair whipping about in the open sports car, Frances felt the day passing in an ecstatic sigh.

It was such beautiful country—a landscape of wonderful fertility, with the purple-tipped ripe green cane and the dazzling contrast of the red ochre fields that lay fallow. This was where all the sugar came from—Queensland, well over a thousand miles of coastline from just below the Queensland border into New South Wales and right up to tropical Cairns fourteen hundred miles away. Once all this backbreaking work of harvesting the cane was done by kanakas from the South Sea islands, but by the turn of the century the immigration laws had changed all that and sent the black man home to his islands. Deprived of a coloured work force like the other great sugar-producing plantations of the West Indies and South Africa, the Australian grower, straining under the intolerable sweltering heat of hard labour, had to find mechanical means of harvesting the crop or forget about growing sugar.

Today in the fields massive canecutting machines, like bright red dinosaurs, stood immobile or moved with great ungainly lurches through the tall standing cane. The killing labour associated with growing sugar had been eliminated and now the grower had plenty of leisure and a good life. Those with the financial resources, like Vincent Donovan, channelled some of their money into the other big industry, cattle. Appointing managers to their lush properties beyond the indigo ranges. The brilliant cane to the ranges; the cattle beyond, and on the Tableland where it was more temperate, tobacco. A good life, and for added pleasure and relaxation the breathtaking beauty of the Great Barrier Reef that Nature had taken millions of years to build up, or for a different kind of excitement, access to the world's finest game fishing ground.

Dario turned his splendid head with its Italianate profile and complexion, the tightly curled, splendid head of hair. It seemed quite extraordinary to him now, but he scarcely remembered his cousin as a child. He had been nine to her six, but then it had been Uncle Robert who had managed the home farm and he had gone home to Italy with his mother when he had been seven to nurse his dying Grandmamma Adami. He continued to regard his cousin indulgently. The sun was far more exotic than anything she had been used to for many long years now and he began to feel concern for her beautiful skin. Like silk! he thought, and wanted to touch it. Skin had such marvellous tactile qualities, the sheen and the clean shimmer, the red blood that coursed beneath its sensitive covering.

Without even bothering to slow down, he reached over to the back seat of the car with his left arm and flung his find on to the girl's lap. 'I think of everything, don't I?' he challenged her with his extraordinarily ardent dark eyes.

Too ardent for a cousin, Frances thought, and fingered the wide brim of a shiny green straw coolie hat. 'And how am I going to keep it on as we hurtle along?'

'It has a band, surely?' he asked with gay assurance in the answer.

'Oh, I didn't see that.' Her quick smile irradiated her face and she fixed the thin black elastic under her chin and turned to him for approval.

'Charming!' he said with serious earnestness. 'You look charming—luminous golden eyes that reflect your bright spirit, a lovely mouth, wide and mobile. I couldn't view you with anything else but admiration. By some impossible good fortune I now have a lovely, seductive girl as a cousin, but I can't have you covered in freckles.'

'I *don't* freckle, my dear, thoughtful cousin!'

'Then I'm done for,' Dario said lightly. 'Vanquished before I've begun. You're beginning to be too disturbing an influence in my complicated young life.'

'Too much sun on your head, *mio caro*!' she said in a sweet teasing fashion, her eyes on his bold classical profile with a strong look of his mother but without the unnatural black glitter of his mother's eyes. 'We both know how irresistible you find pretty girls.'

'And why not?' he said with a hard persuasiveness. 'Has my mother been talking?'

'I drew my own conclusions, *cousin*. I'm not a bad judge of such things.' She gave him a swift, sidelong smile. 'Besides, if you're thinking of starting a flirtation with me, it's doomed from the start.'

'Cruel. How cruel! A splinter of ice in my heart when I don't feel like a cousin at all. I don't even look like one. No one would think we were linked by any relationship of blood. You're a Donovan—and don't look at me with those wide, innocent eyes. I'm an Adami. Different mothers, of course. It makes it all right, I think!'

'What on earth are you talking about?' She looked at him with a faintly troubled expression.

'Cousins may marry,' Dario persisted with a line of his own. 'Plenty of them do, and most girls are desperate to be married.'

'Well, here's one who's not! Please don't let's talk nonsense, Dario. It's all so beautiful—bravura type country.'

'Like you, *cara*. Wine after water.'

'You're really unstoppable, aren't you?' she smiled.

'Of course, and you are no silly romantic miss. What a pity! I wish you were.'

'I'm your cousin from over the Tasman!' she said, faintly scolding, but all he could hear was the sweet, sensuous femininity of her voice.

'No. You belong here,' he said quietly. 'Can't you see that? This love affair you think you're starting really began in your childhood. I can see from the eager curiosity in your eyes that you don't fully realise it yet, but you seem to me like a flower, a sunflower. Each day you become more radiant, more abandoned. You turn up your face and you don't cover your lovely skin or your hair—but not, alas, abandoned in the way I want.'

'You're terrible!' Frances said with a laugh. 'But I like you—as a *cousin*. Remember our history and forget the romantic part.'

'When I worship you unreservedly?' His black eyes sought her own, a smile hovering around the edges of his mouth. 'As our grandfather worships the name of Donovan. Into our lives you've brought colour and a certain amount of confusion. Already my mother is rethinking her plans and Grandfather looks ... acts ... so much better. There's a softer note to his voice. He doesn't so often cut me to ribbons. He's a demon taskmaster, you know. Today we are together with the freedom to enjoy everything. You're mine, and I can't lose sight of you.'

Some serious note in his voice took Frances off guard and almost for a moment she stopped smiling. Dario, ever sensitive to change, caught the shift in her attitude and smiled at her with his swift, easy charm, banter alone in his musical voice. 'Peace, *cara*, peace. Peace, peace, peace!'

'But isn't it? The sweet, fragrant earth, the smell of the trees and the rich, flowering soil. It's a great mystery, nature, and this is the Lotus Land.'

Dario's eyes touched her lightly, noting the radiant tenderness. They were moving deeper into the countryside with the sweet, haunting music of the birds running like a thread through the hot drowsy sapphire and gold of the afternoon. It was lush country, very lavish, but casual too, just the way he liked it, the trees shot through with sunshine but deliciously cool beneath.

Suddenly Frances swung her head with blazing vividness. 'Oh, slow down Dario, please. Over there —what a thrilling sight!' The car ground to a halt with Dario, for once, shocked into surprise. What Frances called thrilling was a deeply familiar sight to him—pleasurable, certainly, but very familiar, like cattle grazing. Against the massed jade green of the trees, running splendid and spirited over the thick velvet grass, was a mare and her foal. The mare was a thoroughbred—she had to be, with her extreme legginess and free forward thrusts. A beautiful bay, the head delicate in proportion to the long, sloping body with its thin, gleaming skin. The foal was just a gangly little youngster, incredibly frail and unsteady on its finely sculptured legs but born to run free.

'The swiftest creature in the world!' Frances said admiringly.

'No, *cara*!' This very gently.

'*Yes*. The thoroughbred can maintain dazzling speeds for up to two miles, you know. Even the cheetah would become exhausted within a few hundred yards. There's something so utterly beautiful about a horse, isn't there?'

'I see there is,' Dario said smilingly. 'Different things make my heart fill with glory, *piccola*. Your fresh, natural beauty, for instance. Delicate, elegant proportions. The artist's eye, you see. I must show you my father's sketchbooks. He shared your enthusiasm for horses. So does Sutherland. He owns this vast setting—David Scot Sutherland, the big man around here—but don't for the love of God say that to Grandfather!'

'No,' Frances answered, instantly comprehend-

38

ing. 'He breeds horses, of course, Sutherland?'

'Yes. Thoroughbreds and quarter horses too. He's starting to specialise in them. There's a big market for them with the cattle kings. They can't be matched when it comes to cutting out cattle. They're smaller than the thoroughbred with a more powerful physique and a terrific turn of speed up to the quarter mile, hence the name. Very good-natured too. Dave got quite a bit in the papers just recently. He paid the top price for an imported American stallion at the last Sydney sale —a phenomenal price, but he's got plenty of it. He's got a few Arabs too. Pure Arab, I mean, no mixing the strain—that would be unforgivable. He cherishes them pretty well, like Grandfather does the Rolls-Royce.'

'Well, it's perfectly understandable in its way. The modern horse owes just about everything to the Arab. I bet those two there have Arab in the background.' Frances turned her bright head. 'I can see all the glistening white fences, but where's the house?'

'About a mile back through the trees. You can't see it from here. A nice old place at that! The funny part is, Dave made his entrance from nowhere, as mysterious as you like with plenty of hard change. He was an engineer, I believe, building bridges in Argentina or some such place. Next thing he's here. right on our doorstep, so to speak, and trying to gobble up that. He's after the farm.'

'Sugar Hill?' Frances asked in surprise.

'Granddad will have his hide first, and he's still a crack shot. Not that they don't meet as civilised gentlemen, with neither of them no such thing. But Dave's a man of ambition. He wants to spread out and he doesn't take no for an answer. We're producing more than enough sugar and he owns all the land in between. One by one they've sold out to him. For my part he can have it. We could go anywhere, do anything. I'm no farmer—I hate it!'

'But you must love your environment? It's so grand and beautiful.'

'I do, yes. But there are other places, *cara*. A big, wide world, and I'd like to see it some time. Life hurtles past like the midnight express after twenty-five—and I'm that! So far I've had my nose to the grindstone, or as close to it as I'll ever get, so don't smile. Hard work killed my old man. Study too— he was a damned good botanist. They came to him for miles around for advice about nutrition and disease and pests and every damned thing. Sugar is the largest agricultural undertaking in this State and he knew a whole lot about it, yet he obeyed Granddad as if he was the Lord God Jehovah. Your father got out but not mine. He toed a straight line under trying conditions and what did he get? Dead at fifty-two—a massive heart attack. We brought him in from the fields. Granddad didn't open his mouth. Not one word for a week. I won't say he didn't feel it for an unfeeling old man. Just think of it, Frances Donovan—a whole life devoted to a mountain of sugar. A colossal mountain of sugar cane. It's so utterly, damnably, impossibly priceless. As it is, I have the great good sense to do next to nothing. What's it all about, *piccola*, I ask you? When all our hopes end in defeat.'

'Perhaps Uncle Desmond had his own vision,' Frances said, her eyes filling unexpectedly with tears. 'The eternal quest for a sense of fulfilment. Maybe it doesn't matter so much if we don't find it so long as we keep on trying.'

'But then you're a girl of character!' Dario said

softly, and obeyed the totally irresistible urge to touch her cheek. 'Your skin is like silk!'

'Thanks to the hat,' she said quickly. 'Your talent alone imposes a kind of debt or responsibility, Dario.'

'My talent!' he said rather scornfully, but he knew quite well he had it. 'Life is so short, as I see it, our responsibility is to enjoy ourselves. And that's exactly what I intend to do.'

'Grandfather thinks you're going to enjoy yourself right here, at Sugar Hill.'

'Well then, my lovely one, he can keep right on thinking that. I won't disillusion him. Neither will Mamma. Did you ever see a more desperately dogged woman? When the time comes we'll move out.'

'And what will happen to the property?' Frances asked, her eyes on the emerald green slopes. The mare was quiet now, cropping over the grass, the foal at her feet.

'Sutherland will buy it, of course. What else? I'd sell in a minute, and Dave is a man who usually gets what he wants. I tell you, *bella* Francesca, you nice little girl, the exodus is about to come. It will be a relief. My mother acts like a miracle of fortitude and calm, but it is an act. I know her—wholehearted discipline, and it's not her at all. She's elemental like me, but much more character, determined. Underneath it all she's in a rage of impatience. Another woman would have been at breaking point, but not Mamma. There's always the moment when we must begin to live, but I lack the power and the courage to make a move on my own. I can depend on myself for nothing. With money it will be different. For me, for Mamma, for you, perhaps, *piccola*. Sugar Hill has exacted a pretty stern tribute after all—Donovan's sons, both dead, the Old Lion still on the prowl.'

Frances looked at her cousin very searchingly. 'I think there's a dormant resolution in you, Desmond—Dario—Donovan, for all you like to deny it. It's made no demands on you as yet, that's all. Under that gay, mercurial front there's a deep stream of gravity. There *has* to be, because I believe, if you don't, that you have real ability. It's little short of a crime to waste it. I can see you want to study.'

'Study, no!' Dario threw back his glossy black head and laughed. 'You see too much in me, *cara*, like my mother. I'm hopelessly lazy. Don't try to remake me. My formidable Mamma is enough. The strength of her! She'll never give up, like a juggernaut.' He looked at Frances, his black eyes lightly smiling. '*La vita e nel tripudio!* There's naught in life but pleasure *angiola mia*. Now you, like Mamma, are beginning to think about improving me. Does no one in this world love me for myself?'

'I would say your mother, to an extreme,' Frances said equally lightly, but very seriously indeed. 'Certainly she's very ambitious for you in the way many mothers are. The thing is, Dario, if one wants to be successful at anything, the job has to be taken seriously—real effort. Nothing is easy even for the highly gifted. In fact they're just the ones who work hardest of all. A gift must be matched by a powerful driving force. Perhaps in your case it might be your mother.'

'Or a wife?' Dario asked with a long sideways look.

'The question doesn't arise here, *caro*.'

'I accept the challenge!' said Dario, his eyes black and taunting.

'And I'm changing to a safer topic,' Frances

smiled, and turned her head away looking over the rolling green slopes. 'Tell me more about this David Scot Sutherland. It's rather a mouthful. Where did the "Scot" come from?'

'*Scherzati*! You're joking, little one. Dave's grandfather was an engineer. He came out from Scotland as a young man on some job and finally settled in Victoria.'

'Well, I suppose at least eighty-five per cent of our grandparents came from the British Isles. We're not exactly pure-bred Aussies. Look at you! I might see you every other day strolling along the streets of Rome.'

'Always in the company of a beautiful woman, one hopes. Dave, now, belongs to a whole Sutherland clan, but he's the only one who strayed up to Queensland. Geoffrey Sutherland is his cousin.'

'Not *the* Geoffrey Sutherland, the architect?'

'The same one. He drew up the plans for Dave's house. Supervised the work no less, and he's a very busy man, but devoted to Dave. They look more like brothers than cousins—a strong tribal stamp. They're proud and handsome, black-visaged devils, but Dave's got glacial eyes, if there was ever such a thing. They're pure chunks of ice, especially when he's on about something. He's got quite a temper, but he's never dull. In fact, he fascinates me like everyone else. He's quite a force around here, everything going for him—the success you were talking about, charm, sophistication, energy. He's a complicated guy, but classy, very definitely classy.'

'Sounds marvellous!' Frances murmured, not really liking the sound of him at all.

'Chances are you won't like him at all.' Dario momentarily frowned. 'I've an idea Dave thinks a woman's main role is seduction. He likes it that

way, but it bothers him not at all. He's one of those
bachelors with the best of both worlds. You know
the saying, when the sun comes up there's work to
be done, man's work, and hang the little woman.
They only get in the way!'

'Marvellous!' Frances said again, her eyes smoky
amber.

'Oh, don't let me put you off him,' Dario said
happily. 'He's quite a character, Dave. I admire
him greatly, but I don't get too near him in case he
slashes me to ribbons, like Grandpa. Dave's blasted
me in the past. I've the notion he finds me little
more than a loafer—letting the property go, not
taking sufficient interest in Grandfather's affairs,
which God knows I don't. But he does like my
work, my painting. Believe it or not, two of my big
canvases adorn his walls—an accolade in itself, in
fact, some might think they were made. Two
Adami originals in a Sutherland house!'

'Adami?' Frances swung her satiny head to look
at him.

'That's the way I sign my name. I'm more an
Adami than I'll ever be a Donovan.'

'How odd!'

'Not at all. It's what I said—the strong tribal
cast. You couldn't be anything else but a Donovan.
Perhaps that's why the Old Man loves you so much.
Certainly he has no great love for me.'

'Don't say that!' she said, troubled and unhappy.
Dario covered her hand with his own and she
didn't move away. She could never help him understand what she didn't understand herself. All the
savage and unholy energy that had burned in her
grandfather as a young man had left him little time
for tenderness. It was not that he had no natural
inclination. He had been her wonderful confidant

as a child, a fount of wisdom with an immense capacity for secret conversations and exploring the mind of a child. Perhaps he was one of those rare people for whom only one person had the key—for her, a sad distinction, because her own dear father had missed so much love and understanding. Vincent Donovan was quite obviously a man who inspired love but rarely, if ever, returned it, a most curious and pitiable thing.

She turned to her cousin with the wonderful clarity of wide amber eyes, speaking to him gently, slightly shaking his hand. 'Don't let's sit here brooding about what can't be undone. The capacity to love is a great blessing. And you have it!' she said with finality. 'Don't think, either, that I won't badger you about your talent. It's a great responsibility and I suspect you've had the odd moment when it's clung to you with a kind of desperate tenacity. Some things are stronger than we are.'

'That's evident, *cara*!'

Before she knew what he was about Dario thrust his strong brown fingers through her hair and kissed her lovely mouth with a strange and very sweet familiarity so that when he released her she could only give a breathless, wry smile. 'I suppose I asked for that!'

'You did, *adorata*. I'm so glad you came!'

CHAPTER THREE

SCOT SUTHERLAND swept into Frances' life with all
the force of a tropical cyclone, overflowing with
fury and enormous, unpredictable vitality—an ava-
lanche, as thoroughly male as a male can get, and
she hated him on sight, an ecstasy of antagonism, a
fever and fret without precedence in her young
life, with far-reaching consequences for herself. All
the hundreds of people she had met in her short,
sheltered life simply vanished before the onslaught
of this intolerable man and not for a moment did
she question the faint tension of hysteria he en-
gendered in her at that very first meeting. Even the
memory passed across her with a disturbing shud-
der.

The day began mildly enough with the whole
house seemingly at peace after a sleep disturbed by
Dario's return to the house in the early hours after
what might have been, had he the money left, an
all-night card game, a pretty well weekly thing
with a few of his 'wild mates'. Rosa, who so named
them, had been disturbed as well, strikingly picturesque in a peacock-hued dressing gown, eyes
glittering with great passion, her great rope of jet
black hair swinging across her noble breast, a tortured woman, very voluble, all Italian, big shapely
hands gesticulating, thanking the Almighty that
Vincent Donovan was sleeping the deep sleep of
the very old and children. Think if he had been
awake to witness the lamentable fall from grace—
again!

Dario, being Dario, was still engagingly affable,
even under the weather, very easily led away by his

mother, kissing two anxious faces with ears trained to the left wing of the house, 'Goodnight!'

'It's *morning!*' Rosa had said in a tone of extreme exhaustion, having talked herself out, with Dario attempting caution:

'Be calm, Mamma. How you suffer! It's true, it's morning, but you find me still alive. *Dormivi, Francesca? Perdonate.*' Black eyes very ardent, sparkling with some hidden excitement, undiplomatically swaying on his feet even with one arm around his mother's ample waist.

In the end they all padded to their rooms to fall into deep, soundless sleep, not for a moment prepared for the surprise of the morning, the only piece of good fortune being Vincent Donovan's triumphant weekly ride into town to see his old crony and lifelong physician, almost as old as himself, but doing better than most in keeping up with the staggering wealth of scientific data to hand.

Frances, by nature and training methodical and tidy, longed to impose some kind of order on the extensive grounds that had once been so beautiful. The last few years had seen a great change, starting with the catastrophic, untimely death of Uncle Desmond, Dario's father. He had been a Donovan, even if his son wasn't, but Frances had promised herself she would enlist Dario's help on the motor mower at least. In a way, the appalling-sounding Scot Sutherland was right—Dario *was* lazy. If the vegetation wasn't cut away soon, they would have snakes on the veranda. Chris, now, would have had the place looking like a parkland with all the voluntary help in the world from herself and her mother. As a family they loved that sort of thing and they had a beautiful garden of their own, but not, of course, on the vast scale of Sugar Hill's private grounds which covered about four hectares of natural bush and fern gully once contoured with gravel paths and steps of rocks and outcrops of moss-covered boulders in free and forceful arrangements and all kinds of colourful plantings: vivid little daisies, harlequin and passion flowers, the pink, highly perfumed Rangoon creeper and the jasminium grandiflora from India, both rampant climbers. These had gone wild and the pockets of flowers died away. Only the great shade trees imposed their own discipline—the spectacular beauties of the tropics, magnificently ornamental when given the necessary space of a very large garden, the deep rich soil and the humidity they craved. There were trees, too, that had come from tropical Asia, the West Indies, India and Africa and even the Congo. None of the cool climate trees and shrubs Frances was used to. New Zealand had supplied Australia with many outstanding varieties and they were grown as far north as Brisbane, but not in the humid heat of the far north.

Today she would confine her activities to within a few hundred yards of the house. There was a shrub there with a brilliant mass of yellow flowers, but it wasn't being shown to advantage at all with some kind of ground cover endeavouring to turn into a climber and pull it down. She hadn't brought anything in the way of work clothes, not anticipating the need, and nothing of Rosa's, who was built on Venus de Milo lines, would look anything less than grotesque even if Frances felt able to ask, which she didn't. Finally she settled on what would least show the dirt and protect her legs from the thick, cutting grass at the same time: denim flares and a cheerful yellow shirt. How she did it no one would have known, but the whole look was one of careless, uncontrived elegance, not workmanlike at all.

Dario didn't think so either, standing on the veranda, his hands clasped lightly above his head, in his eyes an expression of affection and vast admiration which quickly melted when she outlined her intentions.

'What is this big thing in your life, work? Do you not wish to enjoy yourself?'

She laughed softly and pushed him down the four timber steps. 'I will be enjoying myself, don't worry. What I can't understand is how you can bear to leave the grass grown around your ears.'

'But I'm so busy, *cara*, all the week. You can't expect me to start on the house. That's woman's work.'

'Not this little lot,' Frances said soberly, surveying the incredibly lush jungle. 'Why don't you get somebody in if you can't do it yourself? I mean, Grandfather has a position to keep up. Sugar Hill was a showplace in my father's day.'

'Grandfather doesn't give a damn, not these days. He's too old. Don't you understand, little one? He's gone right past caring about long grass and position, and I'll never care!'

'You lazy layabout,' she said sweetly. 'If you can't change, you can't, but you can help me, can't you? That I care is evident. Won't you help me, please?'

Dario stood distractedly for a moment with the sun glinting on the thick coils of his dark hair, a frown between his black brows, a man contemplating a bleak horror. 'All right, *cara*. On one condition.' His brilliant smile broke out, flashing, and Frances ran on down the steps past him.

'*No!*' She shook her bright head, her own golden vitality, the expression in her eyes in contradiction,

49

alive with an ancient promise.

As seductive as thrilling, fragrant as a flower, Dario thought tenderly, and perhaps too spirited, too precious, for rough handling. 'It looks like a rotten awful mess to me,' he said with something like anguish, 'but I'll at least get the mower out. Once you get the hang of it,' he said maliciously, 'you'll be all right. I know an incredible little spot where we can cool off later.'

'And that, my dear cousin, is just the spot we're not going.' Frances spoke firmly, very kindly, as authoritative as a mother.

'Where, *where* do you want to start?' Dario asked with ludicrous obedience, then with immense dignity walked off to the old stables where the gardening equipment, almost rusty with neglect, was kept. Even an hour's work made a fantastic improvement, and Frances felt almost gay with delight. Such a joy to restore some order to the old place. Dario hadn't spoken for the best part of the time, not under the same magical spell—shirt off, beautiful bronze back gleaming from the unexpected toil, a baffled look on his face. Such a programme wasn't reasonable and there was no pay in the arrangement. Frances, busily happy in her little adventure, decided to keep him at it. Another hour and they wouldn't know the place. Already Rosa had come out on to the veranda, first with unwilling interest, then with a great burst of laughter.

'The sacrifices one makes for love! My poor boy, such suffering!'

'It looks good, doesn't it?' Frances called, the sun slanting across her beautiful hair, about her a look of radiant happiness, but Rosa only gave a faint smile.

'Better give him a cool drink before he expires.

He seems to accept your dictatorship. Isn't it always the way?' Then she turned and walked away, locked in thoughts of her own.

A long wail broke from Dario: 'Water!' and Frances dropped the rake with smiling pity and ran up into the house, beautifully graceful, as self-possessed as ever, calling that they would have a morning tea break under the poinciana—ten minutes and no more. Dario received this with two spots of colour high up on his face. If he could get his hands on her he would hold on to her desperately, but all he could hold on to was the motor mower. Still, she was right, it did look very nice, and perhaps Grandfather might spare him a few words of praise. It was swelteringly hot and afterwards he would make sure she would follow him anywhere. He himself was in the grip of a kind of paralysing excitement. He scarcely knew what he was doing or saying for that matter. After last night. . . .

Frances, in the kitchen, made a jug of iced coffee, very strong black coffee, with scoops of ice-cream, whipped cream for the top with a dash of cinnamon. Dario liked it that way. There was nothing in the way of cake. Rosa cooked only very savoury food. Grandfather didn't eat sweet things at all, and if she wanted a cake, which she sometimes felt like, she would have to make one herself. There were chocolate biscuits in the refrigerator. Dario must have bought those, for he had a very sweet tooth. She would make him some sandwiches—nothing dainty, he would laugh them to scorn. Big, man-sized ham and mustard with perhaps a slice of tomato. At all costs she had to keep him at work. The chance might not come again and she, if no one else, would lose her sanity if a snake got into the house.

As she moved about quickly with a tea towel draped around her, her tilted amber eyes were full of eagerness and a genuine affection for this newly found cousin of hers. It would be impossible not to like Dario. He might go right out of his way to sound senseless at times, deny his undeniable talent, but a little aggression on her part might work very well. One couldn't afford to drown a gift of that magnitude in an indifferent morass. When the grounds were to her liking, without breaking both their backs, she would start on Dario's real work, his painting. The few canvases she had seen were quite enough to earn her interest and persistence. With more than average graphic ability herself, she knew a superior, very real talent when she saw one.

Dario's paintings had a reality he, the man, seemed to lack, though they showed a certain 'rebel' quality. There was clarity there and an engaging candour and a quite definite ability to handle paint. Plenty of room for development, perhaps, but by the same token his gift was not in dispute. He spoke of a wide, wonderful world and the world would be a revelation to him. Dario was twenty-five. It was about time he embarked on a serious programme of work and study. Would that she had his fresh virtuosity broken down to a minimum in herself. Ah well!

What really amazed her was that Dario's natural curiosity hadn't triumphed over his circumstances. After all, Grandfather was a rich man. He could well afford to promote his grandson's career. But he was old and his powerful love for the land kept his grandson tied to a destiny for which he had no liking nor any real aptitude. How strange it all was, human destiny, but she was unable to stand by and watch Dario miss his true expression—a revealing illustration of her own mind which was very vital and persuasive and curiously devoid of envy. Such women had provided impetus and inspiration to many brilliant men, an influence that had been acknowledged right down the centuries, but Frances never thought of it as that. She only knew it would give her enormous satisfaction to prove Dario the white-haired boy for once, with the promise of a brilliant career. He had shown his talent even since he had been a little boy. Rosa had told her as much, and Rosa wasn't a woman who allowed maternal pride to interfere with her critical faculties. Rosa had walked the great art galleries of the world and what she had seen made her cling to a glow of hope regarding her son.

With a gesture of her pretty, slender hands, Frances surveyed the finished tray. Even her darling mother would be pleased with her. She picked it up and headed towards the door. No sign of Rosa, she evidently didn't intend to join them. In fact Rosa spent much too much time lying down— but this, Frances tactfully concluded, was none of her business. She couldn't remake the whole world, and Rosa might be saving her energies for the day of deliverance which unhappily would coincide with Grandfather's demise. She wasn't a hypocrite about it. She had announced quite frankly, almost glaring at Frances with old passions and resentments, that 'the time would come!' and they all knew what time that was.

The thought of it even made Frances feel guilty, though she had no wish nor expectation for herself. Certainly her grandfather would remember her, but she would much rather have him alive. Still, she felt no less guilty every time she looked at the Old Man with his increasing air of frailty. Not so

Rosa, who could not pretend. She had given up too many years of her life in his service. Her husband had given his very life. Dario was entitled to all the Old Man had, and more.

Somewhere across the hot sweet stillness and the smell of newly cut grass came the sound of a voice, a hard, masculine voice, formidably sophisticated. A ringing tongue of resonance and power, overwhelming in its self-conviction, so that not for a moment did Frances consider it lunatic. But it held her in a kind of stark disbelief, for it was furiously angry with the sound of impending disaster.

She broke into a half run, scarcely conscious that the contents of the jug were leaping and lapping with a life of their own, ruining all those carefully prepared sandwiches. Something was definitely wrong, and Dario was involved. It simply wasn't in her nature to play the part of the detached spectator.

In a near frenzy of impotence she banged down the tray on a lovely walnut credenza and ran on out on to the veranda, a small elegant arrowhead of attack and impatience. What on earth was happening? What she saw was naked fury. It shocked her into inaction and numb horror. Dario, as vacant as an idiot, was being strangled by a savage, a powerful, handsome man with wide shoulders and the narrow hips and long legs of an athlete. This was no equal match. Dario had little hope against this wild man, who only needed a machete between his hard white teeth to complete the picture.

Dario, a doomed man, looking upon *la dolce vita* for the last time, yet managed to turn his head towards Frances as though she was his last possible hope. It was all that she needed. The whole world was reeling about in a shimmering blur, but she didn't hesitate, not even for a fraction of a moment. Someone would have to stop this tall, raging beast—raven hair, dark bronze skin, *very* tall, but thoroughly Italian with a volcanic temper. He too turned his head at her impetuous flight and flashed her a glance out of the most incandescent eyes she had ever seen—brilliant, blazing, winter ice in the tropics! Not an Italian in his whole ancestry, but a man Celt from way back. The diabolical Scot Sutherland. There couldn't be two of him. Dario's description hadn't been far-fetched at all. He did have glacial eyes—and what a contrast with that fiery temper!

Frances' own small face was suffused with bright heat so that she came on like a ruffled flower caught up in a high wind, her heart beating frantically against her rib cage. Just who did he think he was coming here? Strangling Dario, no matter what he'd done—and she had the dismal notion he'd done something. The hard brown muscular arms were tightening, the very white straight teeth bared in anger. Even Dario was looking at her in startled attention. She blew on towards them so radiantly angry she looked as if she too might catch fire.

It was all over in a blinding flash, the charge and the confrontation, a totally unconsidered reflex action, the instinct and compulsion to protect her cousin removing all thought of unpleasant reprisals for herself. Sutherland was looming enormously over her, but at least Dario was temporarily saved from impending death.

'L-l-let go of him! L-l-let go of him, you blackhearted demon!' She seemed to be stuttering with a wild excitement. 'Leave him alone!' Ineffectually she clutched at a hard, long arm, conscious at last that she was being subjected to a terrific scrutiny from those remarkable light eyes, ablaze with arrogance and surely not ... amusement? He was the most decisively masculine man a woman would ever have the misfortune to meet, and antagonism was building up inside her at a frightening rate. 'Bully! You're a disgrace!' she sang out at him like a brave child.

'And you're the most interesting heiress I've seen!' Hands caught her narrow waist in an iron grip, and with shock came the knowledge that she couldn't fight out of it. He lifted her like some *enfant terrible* and in an instant of pure terror Frances wondered if he might fling her down in the lake—a green, ignominious defeat. She *was* falling over a ravine with that hot pulsing of fright, then he deposited her none too gently on the white brick wall nearly as high as herself that bounded one side of the house.

'Sit up and shut up!' He spoke very softly through gritted teeth, a very emphatic command and very well bred. There was a look of elemental sexual antagonism on his piratical dark face, the male for the female—but he wasn't a pirate at all. Obviously he was of royal blood. To cover her trembling Frances jutted her chin, trying to stare him down, but not for the life of her could she brazen it out—a most curious, demoralising thing.

Dario, the unpredictable extrovert, who would always fall on his feet and leave his would-be defender to flounder, set the spark to the conflagration, throwing back his glossy black head and giving a loud guffaw of delight. It was all so achingly impossible! Frances thought. Men were grotesque, no sense to any of their actions, attacking one another, then laughing like lunatics. Even the light, insolent eyes, so piercingly intent on her, had lit up with a kind of sardonic humour. It was too much, too much to bear. For all she knew she too might belong to the purple and honour had to be satisfied. She went petal-white under her golden tan and lashed out with no time to think. She hit hard for all her small hand and the imprint of her fingers showed clearly on his dark polished skin. Fright shot through her with quick fire at the look on his face. Such a thing had never happened to him before, she was quite sure of that.

'Red, the fire sign!' he said, in a hard, clipped voice. 'The mad passion of youth—and you're full of it!' His fingers tightened on the bright whorls of her hair. No woman he couldn't subdue. His hand closed on her nape, tilting her head. There was not time to move or even think, her heart was in a tumult, her face flushed rose, her startled eyes a wide, smoky gold. He gave an odd little laugh and bent his irreverent dark head, finding her soft, parted mouth and kissing it hard—a wild, sensuous, intolerable thing so that when he released her Frances wiped the kiss away vigorously with the back of her hand like a furious child at some ghastly cruelty.

She was almost choking with outrage so that she started to stutter again—she who was noted for the clarity of her speech.

'H-h-how dare you! *H-h-how dare you?*' she said very low, and her voice had lost all its sweet young assurance. 'You're a . . .'

'. . . low cad. Just a low cad, Miss Donovan, definitely not a Campbell. That joyless little act of yours, which certainly didn't lack courage, wasn't the act of a lady. I suppose it *does* make up for your cousin. Dario doesn't even know how to defend himself, let alone retaliate.'

'Be fair, Dave!' from Dario.

'*Fair!*' Frances nearly fell from the fence in her scorn, but the same hateful hands steadied her and she found herself looking into those brilliant incandescent eyes again. 'Thank you!' she said with lofty courtesy, a princess to a commoner.

'Delighed.' He taunted her with his eyes. 'You're a bright, jewelled thing, Miss Frances Donovan from over the seas. Some might say a foolhardy little firebrand—but no matter. The years will take care of that fiery disposition, though you could do with a little control now. I've no real objection to a spirited, excitable little filly, but always control. It's indispensable!'

'I'm not a horse, Mr Sutherland!' she pointed out with exquisite certainty.

'No!' The light eyes flicked over her. 'But consider the old saying—no good horse has a bad colour. You're all colour, plenty of red, bright copper and gold, but next time—and knowing Dario, there will be a next time—don't fly to his defence before you acquaint yourself with the facts. Your irresponsible cousin here, who by a sheer saving fluke happens to be a good if reluctant artist, stole my best colt last night, rode him a good two miles away, without a saddle—and for what? A cheap bet, settle a gambling debt. Risking injury to one of my top thoroughbreds. I don't give a damn if he breaks his own neck or finishes up in the clink, but he's not touching my horses, not without my permission. Of course, that's what made the bet. Pinch one of Sutherland's horses—that would go over big with his fool mates, and this impressionable young idiot took the colt. My best! I could kill him with my bare hands, only the colt's all right. It just tipped the scales in his favour.'

'You very nearly did!' Dario protested, wryly easing his neck.

'Rubbish! I haven't even started on you yet!' There was a faint banter in the dark-timbred voice and Dario visibly relaxed.

'I'm sorry, very sorry, *amico*. Such a thing will never happen again. You have my word.'

'I don't need it. There'll be no next time, not with me.'

'I can't think what came over me!' Dario murmured, showing for the first time some signs of shame. 'Of course I was drunk.'

'Of course.'

'Well, I think you're disgraceful, both of you!' Frances snapped, still touched with a queer glittery rage, her mouth burning.

'Yet you'd pit your slight balletic strength against mine?'

'I was hoping right up until the very last minute that you'd retain some vestige of civilised behaviour, Mr Sutherland.'

'I beg your pardon.' He bowed with languid grace. 'I'd be the first to admit that you might be invincible in some departments, Miss Donovan, but hand-to-hand combat isn't one of them, delightful as it has been. Now, anything to make amends. This could have come at a more suitable moment, but we can't always pick them. Would you do me the honour of coming to a party I'm giving on Saturday evening? A few overseas friends and some of the locals. Dario too, of course, though I can't at the moment see why. I'll ask Rosa and your grandfather myself.'

'I say, that's very generous and forgiving of you, Dave!' Dario said in his agreeable fashion, making a quick return from the near grave.

'I'll say!' Sutherland seconded dryly. 'And you, Miss Donovan?'

'I'd walk into the lion's den to see over a Geoffrey Sutherland house!' she pointed out politely, not giving an inch, but pushing back the massy swing of her hair with unconscious seduction.

'Well, this particular lion is well fed,' Sutherland returned suavely. 'It's only on the odd occasion I'm dangerous, while you, I fancy, are a natural hazard for a man most of the time. I can expect you about eight?' he asked with his faultless accent.

'Of course you can!' Happily from Dario, above any act of violence on himself, when Frances would relive these minutes a thousand times.

But Sutherland hadn't finished with him. 'Walk down to the car with me, Dario. You surely don't imagine you're getting off as lightly as that?'

'All right, come on, then.' Dario sounded a little desperate now and Frances flashed him a protective smile. She was always on hand. Sutherland caught the look they exchanged and he smiled.

'Perhaps when you're finished your lawn you might start on mine, Miss Donovan. I can see you're going to be a remarkable influence about the place!'

CHAPTER FOUR

THE night of the party came and Frances found
herself possessed by an odd kind of excitement, a
reluctant hope-dread. She wanted to go, and whisp-
ered the admission to herself, taking great pains
with her appearance—then again, she would much
rather have remained home with Grandfather, who
had professed himself too old and tired for any
more partying, never his forte at any point of his
life.

'But I want the whole town to see you!' he told
Frances, running his finger across her high cheekbone. 'Desmond, too, looks well in evening
clothes!' This as an afterthought with no real love
in his eyes, but there was no use fighting this hurt-
ful indifference and Dario had given up trying.
But Dario—Desmond—looked splendid with his
inherent affinity for trendy clothes and Frances
gladly told him so, willing her affection and enthusiasm to mask the old man's empty amber eyes
trained rather cruelly on his grandson.

Dario was as devastating in his fashion as only an
Italian can be, or an Italian bred out of the wild
open freshness of the Australian bush, almost an
exact replica for some Caravaggio favourite come
to life, with waving black hair, large flashing dark
eyes, fine long nose, full shapely mouth and a perfect, dark olive complexion. A handsome race, Italians.

Rosa too looked resplendent and very foreign in
black silk with magnificent pear-shaped rubies at
her ears and throat. These didn't belong to her.
Vincent Donovan kept them 'God knows where',

but he lent them out for special occasions such as when the family were out on display. It was thought that he had bought them at one time for his wife Ellen, who had borne him two sons before languishing away in a kind of despair with no love lost between her and her stormy, implacable husband.

Frances, on fire with unwilling excitement, looked miraculous, a dream of femininity, very slender and seductive. In some curious way her eyes looked pure gold between their thick webbing of lashes. Perhaps it was the shimmering, champagne-coloured dress with the faintest gold thread running through it, a low-cut bodice held up by the thinnest jewelled straps, a long floating skirt, almost a sheath until she moved, when it swirled in a mist about her feet. Against the heavy early Victorian furniture she looked like some impressionistic painting, trembling a little in a soft haze, incredibly delicate yet glowing with colour—rosy mouth, the pale gold of her skin, the bronze glimpse of her evening sandals, the rich fire of her beautifully cut and shaped hair.

Seeing her son's eyes on the girl, alive with some masculine fantasy, Rosa knew a great wash of unreasoning jealousy. Her voice urging them along was sharp and faintly bitter, risking the old man's anger that could still blaze up on occasions like a great cane fire. But he too was looking at Frances as if only she could supply the answer to what life was all about. Even at that moment he looked entirely happy, something he rarely did, as if nothing and no one else, the whole lot of them, the ones who had gone before, Desmond and Robert, his wife Ellen and the other one, Rae, who had escaped to New Zealand, mattered at all. *Ahi, cruda sorte!*

But soon all that would be over.

Frances, sensing Rosa's deep unrest, swayed towards her grandfather, hugging him around the waist and lifting her face for his kiss which he gave like a benediction.

'The years that we've wasted, my dearest child. Do you love me?'

'You know I do, Grandfather!'

'Then I'm content. You've come back into my life like a great cure-all!' His strong, heavy hand fell on her head.

He had no real intention of hurting Rosa, or Dario, his grandson, Frances could see that. They simply weren't there as real, living, suffering people, just phantoms who happened to inhabit his living room, and all the long years Dario had grown up in his grandfather's sight counted for nothing. It might have warped his personality, Frances thought, but mercifully it hadn't. Only Rosa waited for the day of retribution in her chilling, enigmatic fashion—and really who could blame her? Grandfather Donovan was the strangest, strangest man, demanding love but rigidly withholding it himself. A mighty source of power and energy in his youth and middle age, the fires were disappearing like the red in his thick thatch of white hair. Still, Frances had told the truth. She *did* love him, and that again was a curious thing. One didn't love to order or even where it was deserved. The whole subject was too profound for her contemplation.

Outside in the drive, Dario swung the car around and headed down the broad straight avenue for the open road. 'Dave's parties! Sometimes I think they keep me alive!'

'I feel nervous!' Frances said from the back seat.

Never for one moment, even had she wanted to, could she have ousted Rosa from her son's side.

'No need! ' Dario flung over his shoulder, driving like the wind. 'You look fantastic, doesn't she, Mamma? Intoxicatingly young and very feminine.'

'Young, *yes* ! ' Rosa said bleakly, looking down her fine nose. 'I would not be either of your ages for anything. Never again. Youth is terrifying—its confidence, its self-assurance. Life teaches us otherwise.'

'It's a party, remember, Mamma.'

'Of course. my son. Never would I spoil your enjoyment. Be on fire, if you wish. In that way you share something with your cousin. All I ask is, Dario, that you don't drink too much tonight. and Francesca. not at all. I don't approve of young girl's drinking. A little wine with the meal, no more.'

'Yes. Mamma! ' Dario said dutifully. with no intention of refusing a single drink. His white teeth gleamed against his dark skin. 'We'll be the only ones sober. *piccola*, except Dave who never looks or acts different whatever he puts away. I remember one time . . .'

'That will do. *figlio mio* ! '

A car was coming very quickly towards them, more on their side of the road than their own. and Dario casually honked the horn without giving the wheel a nudge at all. They passed one another within inches with Dario still with his elbow lolling out of the window.

'Marvellous! Keep that up and I won't eat! ' Frances said in obvious criticism, being a careful driver herself.

'My son is an excellent driver. He knows what he's doing.' Rosa said from the front seat.

'At least no one has ever offered to walk. Relax,

64

little one, we all drive like that around these parts. It's not the city, you know!'

And that's how accidents happened on lonely country roads, Frances thought a shade maliciously, but lapsed into silence. Not so Rosa, who began an involved, very confidential conversation with her son, in Italian, very quick, idiomatic Italian, when all Frances knew of that languge was little more than Dario's favourite: *domani* ... tomorrow, little one! They swept on through the sweet-scented night and the trees, a dazzle of stars overhead, bigger, brighter than any she had seen, and eventually they reached the Sutherland stud.

From the crest of the first slope inside the main gates they could see the lights from the house. It was ablaze, but it was very difficult to see the house. It seemed to grow out of the terrain, one with the night and the magnificent shade trees that had influenced the eventual design. All but one had been saved. Close to, past the brilliantly landscaped grounds, Frances could see it was a very contemporary house, more a modern palace.

'Good heavens, it's big!' she said in some wonder.

'About eleven thousand square feet,' Dario supplied. 'Redwood inside and out. The ceilings inside soar to over twenty feet—a terrific volume of space and furnished to match, or rather to scale. Dave's a big man and he likes it that way. Also he entertains a great deal. Most of the furniture is modern, but *good* modern, if you know what I mean—very expensive, a few very fine European antiques. You should have seen the exterior first in daylight. It's rather difficult to make out the design. As you see, the extensive roof line is quite flat, but it projects at different angles with clerestory windows all round letting in a tremendous amount of light and glimpses of the trees. You'll see what I mean when you get inside. The house is really an enormous square surrounding a central court—pool, barbecue, dance floor and informal entertaining area. It must have cost Dave a fortune, I do know that.'

'I like Sugar Hill!' Frances said loyally and truthfully too.

'Of course you do!' This from Rosa in a curious aside.

'Well, give me Dave's place any time!' Dario said lightly, and pulled off the drive amid a whole bevy of very expensive-looking cars.

They had to walk up to the house on a short flight of steps bordered by a combination of horizontal and vertical plants and a pebbled area that led to an ornamental reflection pool lit under water; a feature of the entrance court, flanked by the familiar New Zealand flax, ivy-covered boulders and a beautiful bronze brolga standing realistically beside the rushes. It was very serene and uncluttered, softened by some fragrant white-starred climber Frances wasn't familiar with. The rocks at selected points were very interesting and she wondered where Sutherland had got them from. She would like to use a little of his know-how with their own garden, a natural landscape such as this, only his obviously received loving care. Probably he employed a whole team of gardeners and she only had herself, with occasional help from Dario. Grandfather, she had found, did not like to spend money—something very strange, for he had a great deal of it.

In fact, Frances had discovered, he was very sparing with housekeeping money, which might have led an outsider to believe Vincent Donovan was living on past glory. This was far from the case. He had invested his money wisely and was better off than ever. Not so his family, who were without one or two 'luxuries' others considered necessities. Frances, like others before her, had given up trying to fathom Grandfather Donovan. He simply *was*—a man of strong personality who left a deep impression on anyone who met him. Perhaps he had brooded over the deaths of his sons, living with the fact day in and day out. There was no means of telling. Only Dario wasn't going to fritter away his talent, she was determined on that. One had to have the will and the courage to make something of oneself. She would have escaped long before this. And there it was, but she didn't see it. Dario lacked her own driving vitality, a direct legacy from the old man. Dario might well throw his life away. It was yet to be seen. But she couldn't, ever.

If Frances overlooked this all-important point, Rosa did not. She walked a few paces behind the girl, forever pondering. Soon Dario must marry. She would welcome grandchildren. Already she had the the girl picked out—someone vastly suitable: Maddelana Rossi, a girl of excellent family who had received a good education, a convent education. She was very pretty and womanly and she would have the wisdom to be led by her mother-in-law. Marriages should be approached with great good sense and caution. Conveniently, in her own case, Rosa dismissed from mind that she had applied neither, but Dario certainly would. She would decide for him. The young Francesca posed a problem, a multi-faceted problem, but it was too early to know.

Dario looked behind to see what was keeping his mother and in the end Frances was the first into the wide, spacious foyer. It was floored with a beautiful dark olive marble and sparsely furnished with only a few very good pieces—an English Chippendale iron chandelier, very unusual, suspended over a very large, circular antique table on which stood masses and masses of the yellow-gold hybrid tea rose Buccaneer, in a wonderful antique container about eighteen inches in diameter. On the far wall was the only other adornment, a very big canvas, skilfully framed.

She could almost walk into it. There was no mistaking what it was, painted directly from nature— the lake at Sugar Hill with the white rambling homestead in the background, not as it had been in its magnificence, but as it was now, surrendering to nature. Frances quite forgot her nervousness, the sound of music and laughter from within. She walked closer to the painting. It created an enormous impression on her, almost inspiring a mood. The colour quality was beautiful. She could never paint a picture like that in her whole life, and she had hung a few attempts of her own, quite pleasing really, but nothing like this. What an incalculable young man Dario was! In the right-hand corner of the picture, the artist's signature: Adami.

Scot Sutherland, poised at the entrance to the living room, caught her rapt expression. She would have stood out anywhere, but here in his foyer she seemed to belong, mysteriously glowing, slanted amber eyes fixed on the painting with a kind of drugged brilliance. His mouth tightened fractionally. He too knew the workings of the old man's mind. The name and fortunes of the Donovans were being menaced. The old man had this fierce passion about family, for all he had wrecked his own. This colourful young creature with her vivid, eager air had been brought in for a purpose, and he found himself disliking it. A man of Dario's temperament would consume all her bright energy. She was built for speed, not endurance. She would need care, whereas Dario, essentially tougher, would demand that very commodity constantly from the woman he would eventually marry. One could feel pity for such a candidate with that mother! Scot's light eyes blazed shockingly in his dark, handsome face as he advanced on the feverishly dreaming girl. It was possible that for all her beauty she had no brains at all, willing to be trapped in this net the old man was throwing about her.

He caught her bare silky arm and she visibly trembled, as curiously conscious of him as he was of her, yet they studied one another as antagonists. He, almost cynically worldly; she rather innocently refusing to be daunted. He gave a faint smile that gave such life to his firm, chiselled mouth.

'It's mine—I'm sorry, *Frances*, may I? I'm afraid I won't part with it. I can see you've recognised very precisely its importance. The other one is inside. A still life.' His eyes touched her face and bare shoulders like slivers of ice. 'I'm only waiting until such time as Dario paints a woman. I've a feeling he could make certain skin shimmer with light.'

And you make my heart beat so fast it's hurting me, she thought, glad of the few minutes' respite when he turned his dark head to welcome Rosa and Dario who were admiring the chandelier.

'*Signora*, how nice to see you again. Dario, my friend!' He bent his head to Rosa's outstretched hand with no trace of awkwardness but a great deal of finesse, so that Rosa beamed, a transformation Frances had never seen. Rosa, in her late forties,

69

was still a splendid-looking woman, and smiling, almost unrecognisable. 'Frances was just admiring your landscape, Dario.'

'*Your* landscape, *amico*. So good of you to buy it, for part of me goes with it!'

'Not good of me,' Sutherland amended. 'Sound. It gives me a great deal of pleasure and I consider it quite a good investment. One of these days you'll wake up to your own talent.'

Dario, with his hands behind his back, was peering into his own painting, not apparently impressed, though he knew it was his masterpiece up to date. He had used rather a lot of white, but it had come off. The whole composition had a translucent glow—the green of the lake, the ancient shade trees, the house vibrating very slightly in the pervading heat. It was necessary to paint sometimes. He remembered exactly how he felt when he had painted this. The excitement still touched him. He turned about and put his arm around Frances' narrow waist, drawing her to him.

'Some day when I'm ready, I shall paint you, little one. I'm not quite at the stage yet, but it's coming. A naked nymph, a nude,' he said, apparently not in jest, for his eyes were half closed. 'Perhaps in the shade of trees, a greeny-gold background. The beautiful texture of the skin, the sparkle of those faintly tilted eyes, the jewel-coloured hair—I can see it now. What a challenge! A woman is the most beautiful thing in the world!'

Rosa looked very dubious indeed and David Sutherland gave a brief laugh at the increasingly hard seriousness of Dario's expression, and Frances' inevitable wild blush, a mantle of colour, enamelling her satiny young skin.

'You're in no danger, Frances. Dario will stick to

still life for quite a while yet!'

But Dario's eyes had the metallic gleam of purpose, the artist's dissecting eyes, a cool, assessing professionalism and none of his usual ardour at all. 'Beautiful small breasts and very slender elegant limbs. I'm sorry, little one, I'm not embarrassing you?' he came back to the party with a jolt.

'You are embarrassing *me*!' his mother announced very frostily indeed, and Frances tried to speak lightly. It was difficult for her even to move with Sutherland so plainly amused, and at her expense.

'I'm sure there are any number of other models, Dario. I'm still remarkably inhibited in that way.'

'But for art, *cara*?'

'For anything, I imagine,' Scot Sutherland supplied suavely. 'Shall we go in and meet everyone?'

He drew them into the living room and Frances tried to compose herself. Why on earth would Dario start talking about naked nymphs? It was too absurd. Then again, it wasn't absurd at all. It all depended what world one was moving in. And Dario *was* an artist. He was fortunate she understood that. Really, if she considered it, it was quite funny. The best thing she could do was forget it. Rosa was obviously saving up a few telling words for her son's ears. Frances only wished Dario had not said it in front of David Sutherland. That was the part she would rather have missed.

Dario's eyes were the artist's. His were cool male, iridescent ice chips. Frances was certain no man had ever looked at her before in the same way. It was really another case of inflammable personalities, and the man was deplorably attractive. She watched him with an odd expression on her face. Pretty damned grim when one could admire a

71

natural-born enemy. He turned his head sharply, pinning her gaze, flooding her with an irrational feeling of claustrophobia, a wild need to escape when a brief moment stretched into a whole year.

The brilliant eyes narrowed, momentarily intrigued, and he said gently: 'I'm so glad you came.'

'So am I!' she said sweetly, 'and such a compelling invitation.'

'One of many, I'm sure!' he returned suavely. 'You present a most remarkable foil for your cousin. How fortunate that he appears to have taken to you at almost a moment's notice. Not everyone could manage it.'

'It's very good of you to try!' she said swiftly with the spirited air so natural to her.

He gave his rare and devastating smile. 'No need to wonder if that hair owes anything to artifice. You're a definite redhead, terrible to trifle with.'

'I shouldn't worry about it, Mr Sutherland.'

'I'm not worrying,' he said suavely, flicking her with his blazing eyes.

Frances felt irritated and impatient beyond measure, forced to smile as the introductions began, but there was no unnaturalness about her. Her face, her slender body, her whole personality seemed to belong in that beautiful room, glittering with a night-time's brilliance, a party's fraternity, smartly dressed people, some scarcely bothering to conceal the curiosity and speculation attached to her person and her name. Indeed, Frances had the odd notion that she had somehow become the mysterious central interest of the evening.

Certainly Dario was thriving on the backwash of her very considerable success, whether for herself or the fact that she was Vincent Donovan's granddaughter. Money, she had found, spoke a common language and it wasn't an alien commodity in David Sutherland's world. Every visible portion of her was examined and instead of making her feel devitalised, it put her on her mettle, exaggerating her beauty so that Dario, looking at her, felt the urge to paint growing on him with magnetic power —the old impossible compulsion. And now, at a party, the whole composition was sketching itself out on his brain, flaring into his fingertips. The best thing to do would be to commit her to memory. He would not forget.

It was well into the evening, however, before Frances could relax sufficiently to enjoy herself or her surroundings. For such a big house, it was beautifully balanced, conveying a wonderful sense of space and volume, almost a kind of spacial excitement, she supposed, for it was very grand in its dimensions but fluid and inviting as well. It was a Sutherland house, which was to say a piece of exemplary architecture and the ultimate in up-to-the-minute life style. It was like *him* too—dynamic but super-efficient, nothing superfluous. It was a perfect house for entertaining, seeing he did such a lot of it. There were plenty of conversational areas with the best of contemporary furniture, lots of lovely custom-built sofas and some effectively placed antique pieces—of museum quality, Frances felt sure. Chris and her mother would love it. They loved houses and this house was absolutely striking. There were paintings galore, a full-size concert grand, oriental sculptures, an ivory collection displayed to perfection in a plain case, a magnificent Japanese screen and from the dining room sideboard, the soft glowing patina of some superlative silver, Georgian probably, with a richly decorated heavy gauge silver tray. Brought up as she had been to cherish beauty in all its forms, she would have given anything to have been alone in the house and able to potter about and admire at will, but that, she supposed wryly, either now or in the future, would be highly unlikely.

Everyone seemed to be enjoying themselves enormously. All the main rooms of the house had immediate access to the central court with its informal dining area and the huge pool had been covered over for dancing—all at the flick of a switch. Behind the bar-servery was a feature wall of pottery tiles, and she simply had to stop and examine it in detail even among a swirling, laughing crowd. Her mother was an enthusiastic amateur potter and she would have been fascinated by this and the beautiful effects—various oxides, zircon, rutile, cobalt and copper, used between dolomite on iron or felspathic glazes. It was a talking point in itself, although Frances appeared to be the only one at the moment interested in it. Probably everyone else had been to the house before.

It was a largish party and when the initial curiosity had somewhat abated she had been treated to a great deal of charm and friendliness and a whole lot of interest in her adopted home country, New Zealand, though most of those present had passed through it at some stage or another. Only two of the guests stood out for their very unsmiling formality, perfectly civil but actively aloof, both of them women. The one was understandable, for her all-consuming interest in her host flashed out like a whole string of neon; the other was rather a puzzle, for Frances had the feeling that she was essentially a sunny-natured Mediterranean type, very pretty and curvy, with glossy black hair in an elaborate, old-fashioned arrangement, an excessively modest décolletage, denied by a pair of melting dark eyes very soft and feminine and a singularly sweet smile, rather childlike and gentle. Only a wide sequinned belt took advantage of that Italian hour-glass figure. Madellana Rossi—Frances remembered the name because it appealed to her, but obviously she did not appeal to Madellana, though she was of some interest, if those numerous sidelong under-the-lashes glances were anything to go on. They were, wary, watching, and Frances found them vaguely unsettling.

Not so the other one—Patrice something or other. She was very elegant and sexy, though not strictly good-looking, but she certainly knew how to make the most of herself. Ash-blonde hair stood up in a shining crest, very sleek on the neck, about a thin, beautifully made up face. Her dress, long and black, was very smart, very bare, and she had no qualms whatever about displaying her rib cage, for her bosom was mercifully slight and unrestricted by any undergarment whatever, and her back was lovely, a long, polished tan. What really set her apart from anyone else was the hot look of challenge in her russet brown eyes. It said unmistakably that she saw every other attractive woman at the party as a rival in the business of getting a man. Her man. Scot Sutherland—and that was what she called him in a clear, mannered voice that became faintly hectoring when directed at anyone else. Scot. Scot darling, the object of her desires and night-time fantasies. Daytime too, Frances made a shrewd guess. Those rust-coloured eyes, the few times they had rested directly on Frances, had been filled with active combat only lightly masked by a few carefully chosen snippets of social chit-chat, the party jargon. What Patrice felt in her heart she communicated as surely as a softly spitting cat. Keep off. Even the glinting silvery crest stood up like a fighting cock's, hostility towards any likely challenger.

Frances could have laughed aloud. What woman in her senses would contest that particular battle? Scot Sutherland could keep his stupendous charm. Why, his very assurance was quite terrifying. Snapping his fingers at any woman he pleased, but not her. She simply wasn't in his league, and she was proud of it. She was positively aginst him, positively and permanently against him. She liked easygoing, agreeable men, not arrogant, high-handed men who threw out a bright challenge to every woman in sight. The modern prototype of Cesare Borgia or someone—at any rate, an exciting, dangerous man. Men like that turned into absolute tyrants, took possession, aroused every bit of Women's Lib that was in her.

One of her own type of young men, seeing her gazing rather furiously at an opalescent wall, came up to rescue her and Frances went into his outstretched arms with enthusiasm. They had danced once before, earlier in the evening. He was very good, a natural, rhythm in his bones. One either had it or one didn't.

'Honestly, you make magic!' he breathed near her ear.

'Between us?'

'No, by yourself. Poetry in motion. No girl here can touch you, though Madellana's not bad. She's got a fit of the sulks tonight.'

'Whatever for?' Frances asked, much interested.

'You'd put any girl's nose out of joint!' her partner supplied, but he was obviously not going to say any more, enjoying the sensation of perfectly coordinated movements. The girl moved like a dream—looked like one too. What happened next was inevitable to a dancer, probably madness to anyone else. As lightly as an autumn leaf she flew away from him, unaware of an audience, deep in the music, executing a faultless chain of pirouettes, straight and clean, head precisely following her lovely free arm, spinning with great authority and charm, like an imagined journey out into space. Her body, so beautifully placed, held every eye like a magnet, so just for the fun of it, with the advantage of her crisp and assured technique she finished with a few *fouettés en tournant*, emerging with a scarcely breathless sparkle. The sheer joy of movement had flowed into her face, giving her a look of almost lyrical vivacity.

'A dancer, no less!' said a now familiar voice.

'Solo Seal!' she supplied, returning slowly to earth.

'Do dance again for us,' said a third, faintly disparaging voice, defying Frances to do just that, but as Sutherland had so rightly remarked, she wasn't a red-head for nothing.

'What would you like?' she asked the tall, insolent Patrice, meeting the hotly glowing glance head-on.

'Not if you're nervous,' Scot Sutherland drawled lightly, unaccountably amused by something.

'Not at all!' she announced casually. Never admit defeat to this man. 'I've spent many long years in front of far more critical examiners.'

'Good for you!' he said, still with that faint twitch to his shapely mouth. 'If I may, as your host, be permitted to express a wish, something classical in style. I've every recording you could wish for.'

'A recording? But surely that would take too

77

long?' Patrice protested, her long, scarlet-tipped hand at her throat as if something was choking her. 'What about Madellana? She plays the piano quite nicely. A little piece?'

'I don't think a little piece would suit Frances at all. She's quite ready to dance all night, by the look of her. We can only follow in the comet's train.'

'Oh!' Patrice said flatly, her face more suited to a funeral.

'Before we go mad, Frances, dance for us!' Sutherland smiled, his eyes all of a piece with the heirloom silver. 'I wasn't so far out with that balletic strength. You move like a dancer, or a dancing banshee.'

'You've met before?' Patrice bit out incredulously, her eyes like fiery coals, or a woman in a madhouse.

'Of course!' Frances supplied, sweetly blazing. A few more telling words instantly sprang to mind, but accurately reading it, Scot Sutherland took a firm grip on her arm. 'We'll just go away for a little while, Pat. Long afterwards I feel we'll all be talking about this. Now what about it, Francesca— Stravinsky, The Firebird, what? It's a real pleasure to meet a girl who doesn't bump into things!'

By the time Frances had finished dancing her hair was spilling over her shoulders in a wild, silken tangle. It suited her, sheltering her vivid, triangular face. The reflection of intense pleasure still lay across many a face, but Scot Sutherland's eyes were as cool and as bland as a shaft of steel. Her thin chiffon dress was clinging to her like a second skin after that last graceful spin and she seemed to tremble in the brilliant light, while Dario, very proud and entranced with her, his mind seething with sketches, caressed her shoulder, his hand twirling through a lock of dark flame-coloured hair. Almost for a moment Frances fancied she caught a flicker of something in those cool silver eyes, the flash of faraway lightning.

'You're so beautiful, I could cry with it!' Dario said, and laughed. 'With you, *bella* Francesca, I could start a fresh life.'

'Start with something cool for me to drink,' she turned and smiled at him, but his mother had moved across to them and laid a hand on her son's arm, the gesture of a captor.

'That was very good, Francesca!' she said with no warmth at all. 'Dario, my son, you are ignoring your friends this evening—Madellana, for one. You have always been so fond of her. Here she is looking so fresh and pretty, and she hasn't even danced at all!' This with an accusing glance at Frances. 'Don't you think Madellana is pretty?'

'Very pretty. Very pretty indeed,' Frances said truthfully.

'Then go and look after her, my son.'

'Leave it alone, Mamma. I haven't decided anything,' Dario said stubbornly.

'Congratulations! So you're of an age to disobey your mother,' Rosa exclaimed with some drama, a handsome, brooding figure, looking down her straight nose.

'Do go!' Frances said in a direct, affectionate voice.

'We don't need your advice,' Rosa applied a marked snub.

'A quick kiss before it's too late!' said Dario, and kissed his cousin briefly while his mother looked at him as if she could murder him, which was one of the very curious things about her, considering how

79

much she adored him. 'I promised Mamma I would dance with the angelic Madellana, but I'll be back later. I intend to enjoy myself, whatever Mamma says.'

'You used to enjoy yourself with Madellana!' Rosa said heavily, and stalked away without waiting for an answer.

After that Frances was even more sought after, so that the big, beautiful, noisy party threatened never to end. Supper was sumptuous—not that she had much of it, being too keyed up to eat, but she had, she realised, perhaps one more glass of champagne than was actually wise. Dario seemed to have disappeared—certainly not with Madellana, who was wilting with neglect, and Rosa, thoroughly annoyed with her son and her unwanted niece by marriage, had already gone home with a young couple who passed Sugar Hill's front door. They at least had the excuse of getting back to the baby-sitter. Rosa was merely seething with resentment and the prospect of having her plans temporarily unsettled. It would have been far too much trouble for her to conceal her wretched feelings. Too much trouble for Madellana as well, who wore her heart on her sleeve like a talisman.

By one o'clock Frances decided it was high time to go home. Grandfather wouldn't want them to stay out much longer and it would take a good half hour on the road. She shut out all the pleas to stay on and went into the house, avoiding Madellana's round long-suffering eyes looking for Dario. Where on earth could he be? He surely wouldn't go without her. Little did she realise Dario had found a secure 'hiding place', as he thought of it, to sketch an idea that was fresh in his mind. Probably if he delayed putting it on paper it would never come quite like that again. A dancer's moving body, exquisite young grace—but of course the movement must be arrested. With such ideas one had to be very careful, so Dario vanished without a word, and oddly enough at such times, words had no meaning for him. Just line. Even his mother's tongue couldn't have diverted him.

'Why so serious?' a voice asked abruptly, and Frances spun around to look into her host's searing eyes.

It was difficult to remain perfectly calm, but there was something wonderfully compelling about crossing him. 'Is looking for my cousin so serious?' she parried, tilting her head to him.

'You answer that. I rather think he imagines himself at least half way in love with you!'

'Would it be too much to ask what you're getting at?'

'Don't be ridiculous!' The fine, chiselled mouth turned down. 'You know quite well what I'm saying. An unfolding flower would naturally delight anyone of Dario's temperament. Dario is an artist —I'm persuaded to think a very good one. He will come shortly to a full awareness of this. There's no escape from real talent. It's a generally held belief that artists are obsessed with a woman's beauty. They get a deep satisfaction from form and skin tone, radiant colouring.'

'And you're the glorious exception?' she asked with a brilliant, audacious smile.

'Not at all. You're a visual sensation, Miss Donovan. But I think I like you best dancing, in silence. Then I can surrender to your quite definite charm. In conversation, of course, it pays to be forever on guard.'

She bent her head quickly, hoping to hide her

quick flush. 'Would it be a sinful hope to think that I may leave? Grandfather wouldn't expect us to be out too late. Rosa has already left.'

'With the Neilsons. Yes, I know. I rather think she's bothered by her son's obvious attraction to you. One could never hope for a quiet period with you around.'

'May I leave?' Frances repeated.

'I'll take you!' he said, equally hard.

'And leave your guests. *Patrice?*' She couldn't help that. It slipped out before she could control it and she instantly regretted it. She sounded almost jealous, and that was just too absurd. The champagne, of course. She could feel her head spinning and she put one slender pale golden hand to it as though it ached.

'*I'll* take you,' he said softly, and encircled her wrist. No arguments brooked, but she came up with one.

'I can't go without Dario. I came with him.'

'Where is he? I haven't seen him for the best part of an hour. I fancy he can get home by himself. It's reached my ears that you are the apple of your grandfather's eye, unfair as it may seem to all else.'

'I don't like you at all, Mr Sutherland!' she said, the champagne talking.

'I know that, but unlike Rosa, you don't bother me.' The antagonism was there again, gleaming out of his eyes. 'Coming?'

'Do I have any choice?'

'Not with me. I don't like dominant women.'

'I'm not!' she said wrathfully.

'You'd like to be, but you're too small. One can't be forceful and five feet three!' He made a suave, smiling gesture over her head to a passing friend.

'Just running Cinderella here home. Won't be long, Carl. You can keep things going for me. Everyone's welcome to breakfast.'

'Sure thing!' Carl indicated grateful acceptance. He raised the glass in his hand, silently toasted Frances and drank. 'More like Scheherezade. I'm sure I'll dream of you tonight. I've never, never seen anything like that—and me with two left feet!'

'We understand,' Sutherland said dryly, and ushered Frances out through a side door that led to the immense garage and night.

'I feel I shouldn't be leaving without Dario.'

'Would you like to go back? Chances are with some spare time on our hands we might flush him out. He doesn't appear to be equally concerned about you.'

'Let's go!' she said briefly, furious with him and herself. Outside in the tropical night the stars were hovering perilously close. A bird wafted by, wings circling above them. Frances wished she was already home and in bed. Her head was whirling, worse in the night air. The bird flapped lower and she cried out. Scot Sutherland drew her to him like a puppet figure.

'Little fool!'

'You don't like me either, do you?'

'Let it rest.'

Something shone in his eyes that she had never seen in a man's eyes before. 'A silly thing indeed to be going home with an enemy – the first time I think it has ever happened to me.'

'Of course!' he spoke with his usual arrogance. 'Inexplicable indeed to such a pampered young woman, with charm. It makes all the difference. Otherwise, who knows, you might have to walk.'

He lifted his arm and lights flared all along the garage walls. Three cars. He walked towards a white Mercedes, settling her first, then going to the other side, easing in his lean frame, turning his dark profile towards her as he reversed out, turned right, then purred down the drive. Another few minutes and they were clear of the lights of the house, picking up speed, heading towards the open road. He neither looked nor spoke to her and she began to feel uncomfortable. Possibly she had offended him. She sincerely hoped so, as some strange alchemy worked in her. To let a man like that get the upper hand would be to expose oneself to a good many defeats. She averted her profile, taking pleasure in her triumph. She looked enchanting and moody at the same time.

'It isn't a joke about you and your cousin,' he said at last, looking steadily at the road.

She sat bolt upright, the shock great. 'I beg your pardon?'

'Don't be stupid, little cat. The party's over. If you ever listen at all to the voice of common sense, you'd know Dario is quite under your spell, and it won't do, for any number of reasons.'

'None of which have anything to do with you!'

'Perhaps not, but it's tremendously interesting. Your grandfather, of course, knows what he's doing —pretty much what I'm doing, importing new blood.'

'At the risk of repeating myself. . . .'

'You hate me. So you said. Not that I take a great deal of notice of what a woman says. What she does is the only criterion. You must realise that your grandfather has a match in mind, between you and Dario, at the moment the dearest wish of his heart.'

'I don't believe you!'

'You do. At this moment you do. Perhaps not before it was pointed out to you, but now you know. It's profoundly moving, when you come to think about it. You have a great deal to offer a man and a whole lot that needs straightening out.'

'Thank you!'

He laughed and his eyes sparkled like diamonds. 'It was miserable bad luck to run into me, wasn't it? You can hardly expect me to congratulate you at all, though such a marriage would be to my advantage.'

'I know you want Sugar Hill.'

'I do,' Sutherland agreed.

'Then why interfere in my grandfather's plans?'

'I'm damnably unwilling to see a silly little sheep like you sacrificed.'

She stared at his dark profile. 'You can't really be serious about this, can you?'

'Why not? It's about time someone taught you to suffer. You've been spoilt with your many admirers and you're very young.' He flickered a look at her face palely illuminated by the moon. Instead of offending him, he had somehow succeeded in mortally offending her.

'Say something nice to me for a change,' she said tautly, her slight breast moving.

'That might be even more dangerous than annoying you. Intrigue would be sure to follow.'

Frances was breathing unevenly, as unsure of him as any silly sheep of a tiger in the jungle. The oddest craving in her was growing to hit him hard. Who did he think he was, anyway? God, he was horrid! The clean male scent of him came to her and she swallowed cautiously.

'Don't be angry with me,' he said with alarming gentleness, a gentleness she feared more than the arrogance. 'More experienced women than you have been caught in a trap. Emotional blackmail, it's usually called. Your grandfather is an old man, but that doesn't mean he doesn't know exactly what he's doing. This is his latest bold new venture and he's had a lifetime of success in some way or other. What qualities Dario lacks, you can supply. Between you the name and fortune of the Donovans will survive. Quite feudal really, but it goes on all the time. The question is, do you intend to walk right into the trap?'

'Why should it be a trap at all? Dario is very attractive.'

'Any more attractive than young Miller? You spent a great deal of time with him tonight.'

'I wouldn't have thought you'd notice.'

'I notice everything in my own house. In fact I think I've made a tactical error tonight. Hair like yours tells its own story. You most likely thrive on opposition. It's a great pity really, marriage *is* out of the question. Dario is a nice boy, but you? . . . I'm searching for a comparison, but I can find none.'

'How about headstrong?'

'That's fine.'

She laughed in spite of herself and it rippled along her slender throat. 'Perhaps we'll invite you to our engagement party. I'd do a great deal to make Grandfather happy.'

'In that case I'll take you home right away.' He put down his foot, driving at high speed through the nocturnal countryside with its wild, fresh fragrance.

'Why, I'm not tired!' she said perversely.

No reply. Dispiritedly now Frances looked out of the window. Scot Sutherland lost all interest in her.

What frail claim she had had was swept into darkness. Unlike Dario, women weren't his weak spot. 'I'm lucky that I'm leaving in a few weeks!' she said childishly. 'I have my own life, you know, at home in New Zealand.'

'Tell me about it,' he said unexpectedly. 'I know the country well, but I don't understand *you*.'

'I can't think for the life of me why you want to. You seem to find me a trial.'

'On the contrary, you're all we needed around here.'

'Oh! I thought I was very much in the way.'

'Forget it, Frances, you do very well so long as you don't fall in love.'

'What's that?' she asked satirically, tilting back her head.

'A temporary derangement. It does happen!' he supplied with a sidelong glance at her long, creamy throat.

'To *you*?'

'From time to time, so don't sound so surprised. I'm as easily attracted to a pretty face as the next man.'

'No more than that?'

'Not up to date. You're prettier than most, Frances Donovan, but a bit of a handful when you fancy yourself under attack.'

'Well, I haven't carried any placards as yet, but I can well understand how a certain type of man can bring out a woman's fiercely militant side. You, for instance, make me feel quite banner-prone.'

'What did I tell you, little cat? The thing you should remember and most women seem bent on forgetting is, soft disarming ways get a man right on side, play the very devil. Not that you need me to teach you every trick in the book. Fortunately for both of us I can see I'm not going to be treated to many of them. Which is just as well if you're to marry your cousin. Are you?'

'I won't, repeat *won't*, answer that. I don't believe in love at first sight in any case. Hate, yes!' She flung him a frosty amber-eyed glance, but his low laugh cured all that.

'Nasty little girl, but I'm old enough and seasoned enough to be able to handle you.' He beat down her gaze with those silver-grey eyes, right in command, and quietly amused.

Frances put up a defensive hand to her pendant earring, feeling it cool against her hot face.

'Do you want to hear about my life in Auckland or not?'

'Tell me!' he said briefly, and smiled.

So she began talking, telling him about her part of the world, her day-to-day life, her mother and her dear stepfather Chris, all the things they were interested in and the things that they did together. She talked as she hadn't done for ages, but she didn't fully realise this, Scot was so skilful in drawing her out. From time to time he laughed, amused and interested by her chatter, asking questions, and unlike most people, waiting for the answers.

The moon was throwing shifting patterns on the white radiance of the countryside, but beyond the next bend orange flame leapt into the sky. Frances broke off her story about how Chris liked to entertain and sat forward, her face touched by anxiety. 'That's not a fire, is it?'

'Burning off trash,' he explained easily. 'The Campigli place—friendly, hardworking people. The harvesting is on in earnest from now on. They were firing the fields earlier in the night. We can go along and find out. Nothing to worry about in any case, it's probably just flared up again. We should have a good view from the top of the hill. The Campigli farm is contoured.' He put down his foot and the big car picked up speed, climbing easily to the top of the rise. Scot Sutherland turned his head briefly. 'I suppose you knew the pre-harvesting firing is out of favour in some parts of the sugar-growing world, but we've found it to be the only effective method of controlling heavy infestation of pests. At any rate, it's proved very efficient. Beetle borers in Queensland have been reduced to very minor importance, along with the armies of caterpillars and the cane rats and snakes. The C.S.R. are constantly coming up with pest-resistant varieties, but all varieties can be damaged to some extent under certain conditions. The wallabies only come in when their own herbage is scarce, but the white cockatoos have been known to do a lot of damage. They just love to tear off the soft rind and the succulent internal fibres.'

'What about grasshoppers? I imagine they'd be a real hazard around native grasslands. There are a lot in the garden.'

'Well, cane is a very hardy crop, you know. The damage from a few isolated attacks usually looks more spectacular than it really is. Certain years, of course, they come in in dense swarms to systematically pick clean the crop and they cause a great deal of anxiety then, but modern insecticides can handle a sustained attack. Queensland leads the world in crop quality, so be proud of it. It produces the sweetest sugar you can get—a combination of climate and soil. Our dry cool winters have a lot to do with it and the aim of every farmer around here is to produce at harvest a crop with the highest sugar content. You've probably noticed already that if you take two teaspoons of sugar in your tea back in New Zealand, you only take one here. Your sugar comes from Fiji, I imagine.'

'Yes, I have noticed!' she said dutifully. 'It's very much sweeter.'

'To good effect, I hope!'

She turned her head swiftly at his sardonic tone. 'If you're trying to tell me I'm sour, Mr Sutherland, come right out with it.'

'I wouldn't dare,' he said dryly. 'Let's get out.' He pulled the car off the road on to the grassy verge and switched off the ignition, climbing out. By the time he got to the other side she was already starting down the contoured hill, staring at the orange-gold inferno.

'Let's go a little closer, please. I'm fascinated by that wild sweep of flame. It's absolutely savage, isn't it? What a drama!'

She floated away, eluding him, like a wraith or an enchanted vision against that slashing backdrop. The lie of the land was giving her flying feet momentum. She seemed to be hurtling like a moth towards destruction and much quicker than she meant to. For a moment she knew pure panic, but swiftly Scot caught her up, locking one hard arm around her narrow waist, feeling the crazy palpitation of her heart.

'Someone had to cry a halt to that mad flight! God, how you love to flirt with danger! Don't do it—lesson number one, and one that seems to come doubly hard to a redhead. One wonders how you'd react to another glass of champagne,' he added, further humiliating her.

'You're hurting me!' she protested breathlessly, swaying around, helpless for the moment to stand free, so unsteady on her feet she seemed to be.

'Clumsy. Clumsy little cat!' he taunted her. 'Who would have thought it when your every movement seemed charmed?'

'Let me go!'

'Why should I? Now that I have you it seems a pity to waste the advantage. Another minute and you can run away home.'

'That's what I want.'

'No, you don't!'

Frances faltered, her amber eyes falling under the weight of some indisputable truth. She was physically, if no other way, attracted to him. Worse, she was vividly alive to him under moving waves of sensation.

'You haven't forgotten any more than I have!' he said, reading her mind's eye.

She wanted to deny all the pulsing prior knowledge between them, but the words wouldn't come, and when they did come she was stammering. She who never explained was explaining herself. 'If I could only stand up by myself, I'd run!'

'We'll soon fix that,' he said with an intolerable touch of humour. 'I'll take you back to the top and then see what will happen. Don't worry—the night keeps its secrets.'

With the most curious ease, he swirled her off her feet, lifting her against him, carrying her back up the rise. 'You're outrageous, and you're making me dizzy!' she exclaimed, vividly recalling the first time those lean, strong hands had touched her.

'All the more reason to blot everything out in one frivolous, extravagant moment.'

'I don't understand a word that you're saying!' she cried, silently acknowledging that he could win any woman he wanted.

'You *do*. I can feel it, but you love these foolhardy duels. Probably we'll have a whole series of them. It's unthinkable that you should be married off before you can separate the real from your tenderhearted fancies. A little experience never hurt anybody.'

She was on her feet again, but he was taking her slight weight, holding her head hard, twisting her hair about his fingers.

'Why don't you run?' he jeered.

'I don't want to!' she said, fatalistically surrendering to this quivering limbo land.

'You didn't want to say that, did you?'

'No.'

'Then it was quite an admission. You're honest, basically honest. It might save you in the end. Don't you long to know what life's all about, Frances? Shut those wide, slanting eyes—cat's eyes. You even look like a cat—neat, triangular face and just as easy to stroke the wrong way. You're trembling, and there's no need. Just accept this in the right spirit. It will be over in no time.'

But he was wrong. It wasn't, any more than a free-fall through space wouldn't seem like an eternity. His hand slid under her chin, tilting her face to him, his mouth cutting off her fluttering breath. Frances found herself responding to him, yielding young body against him, with an instinct far more sure than any reasoning, all antagonisms subdued. It seemed the most natural thing in the world, not a moment's madness bred out of the deep stillness of the night and the flames, fusing them in some elemental communication that was complete. The kingdom of the senses and no other land like it, once visited, an inexpiable memory to return in one's dreams over and over at night. Pleasure could mount to the threshold of pain, so sweet and so searing, so touched with some little violence that when finally he let go of her, Frances was trembling uncontrollably. Beyond his dark head, the sparkling stars seemed to be crashing to the ground. There was nothing, not one word she could find to say. Words would count for nothing anyway. No one could take this particular moment of time and place away from her. It would always come back like a recurrent dream.

'Magic of magics, she has nothing to say!'

Scot's voice sounded a curious note she hadn't heard before, but she was too deeply drugged with him to put a name to it. 'Not true!' she managed softly. 'I was thinking you compare very favourably.'

He threw back his dark head and laughed, and Frances sighed rather tragically. 'Would you please take me home, David. I realise you excel at these cat-and-mouse games, but I detest them.'

'And I can't think when I better liked the sound of my own name. Come along.'

She walked quietly now beside him. Never in her life had she guessed what an odd, inconsistent, ardent creature she really was. But he was half turned away from her, his broad shoulders blocking out the starlight. To become involved with Scot Sutherland would be to have half feminine Queensland as a rival. One could so easily become addicted to the touch of his mouth and his hands. The very thought filled her with a profound self-discipline.

The stars were spinning slower now and he drew her gently towards the car. No soft violence now, but a remote charm, the other side of the coin. Almost for a moment Frances wished she was more of a woman, able to seduce and be seduced. But that was disgraceful, she thought with a sudden qualm. As though reading her heart again, Scot swung her about, staring intently into her eyes, reading behind them, his own shimmering with light.

'Do you want me to love you properly, Francesca?'

'Never!' she protested, very vehemently. 'And that's not the word! Improperly, you mean, like all your affairs.'

If she expected to disconcert him, he gave a burst of expressive laughter, his eyes gleaming ironically. 'You've grown reckless all of a sudden! One thing is certain, angel child, I refuse to take the bait. The hour is late, though as a matter of fact, in one way you're absolutely right. You ought to be older, then we wouldn't have to waste so much time talking. Come on, you silly child, that's it for tonight. Despite my brave show, you know me too well. I can see you're a girl whose intelligence illuminates every situation. Don't let Dario be your only disaster. You're quite safe with me. Don't let any other thought cross your mind.'

'I'm quite sensible of the distinction, Mr Sutherland,' she said, not moving. 'Dario, for one, would never stoop to guerilla tactics.'

'On the other hand, would you rather not go?' He reached for her rather precisely, as stealthy and sure-footed as a tiger, and she broke out of her exalted state of outraged virtue.

'I'm sorry, I'm sorry!'

'No use struggling, of course. Action is the only answer with you. We both know you didn't mean that about guerilla tactics.'

Bodily he almost bundled her into the car, the original autocratic male, the unforeseen element. In another minute he was beside her, vital masculinity, staring speculatively at her cameo profile. 'I can see there's going to be no good time with you, without complications, but I'm glad of a little variety. Variety is the spice of life, Francesca. I'd almost forgotten there were girls like you about.'

'That's obvious!' she burst out, irrepressibly tart, then faltered at that dark polished skin stretched taut over his face. 'All right, I apologise. I know it's better for me if I don't speak to you.'

'You're dead right! Even silence creates a certain static. Don't worry, Miss Donovan, every friendship has its strains of adjustment. A little give and take on both sides and we might be able to iron out our differences. Kiss me goodnight.'

'I damned well won't!'

'You damned well *will*!' he said, unabashed, forestalling all her efforts to shield her face, his fingers shaping her cheekbone. 'I know you'd prefer Dario, but we'll manage all right.'

'You two-fisted devil!'

'What else do you expect me to be? You're the most provocative little wretch in the world. Close your eyes like a good, obedient girl. At this angle you're likely to go cross-eyed!' He kissed her hard, not kindly, and a million light years removed from the more familiar juvenile techniques she was used to. When he let her go she had apparently nothing to say for herself. She was doing her level best just to breathe normally, making herself small, like a kitten in a tight corner.

Fire and brimstone was what he deserved. But at least he was interesting. Patrice and anyone like her could bring in all the artillery in the world. They were welcome to him with the greatest good cheer and no thanks from anyone. All this was calculated, done purposely, probably to upset Grandfather's schemes. Dismally Frances recognised the grain of truth in his allegations. Her serenity was gone and a blinding perversity was wishing her back in his arms again. Had Scot Sutherland more agreeable manners and a different personality he would be a fabulous man. Worse, yet worse, the relaxed line of his mouth mocked her. Shame, shame on you, she thought, trembling like an overwrought cat. What a dangerous, handsome, unscrupulous devil! It was wisdom to be frightened of a man like that.

The sound of his voice startled her.

'However annoyed you are, would you please stop glaring at me?' he implored in a darkly amused voice.

There was a significant pause, but she had no spirit left to contradict him. She shrugged a little helplessly. She was just a green girl, hopelessly outclassed. 'I'm tired!' she managed, rather moodily. She leant her head back, her hair rippling silkily over the headrest, her breath coming shakily, the very picture of innocent seduction.

'Which is a blessing,' he returned suavely, 'or at least a piece of uncalled-for good luck. If you would only admit it, Frances, you've had a most enjoyable evening.'

She muttered something, her tender young mouth wry, the moon on her pale, triangular face, but whether she was talking to him or to herself, he couldn't tell. Scot smiled a little crookedly in the soft gloom and touched a finger to a button on the dash. Soft music spilled into the fraught interior and he said not a word all the way back to Sugar Hill.

What a foolish child! the smile probably said. Frances didn't care.

CHAPTER FIVE

Rosa met her at the front door in a state of choking anger and resentment, taking in Frances' windswept hair and wild rose flush in one glittery glance filled with furious unrest. 'Where is he? Where's Dario?'

Frances leaned against the shut door, absolutely stunned by the look of hatred that was an unshakable fact. 'I don't know, Rosa,' she said with a grievous lack of what Rosa considered the proper respect but an earnest wish to divert a scene. 'He just disappeared from the party, but I'm sure he's quite all right. You know what Dario's like. He'll turn up. Mr Sutherland brought me home.'

'*Mr* Sutherland, bah!' Rosa went on bitterly. 'I saw how you were devouring him, but you won't catch him like that. It's my son you're being held to account for. Only my son I am interested in. How could you leave without him?'

'How could he disappear?' Frances snapped sharply, her quick temper rising, though she looked and felt very small against Rosa's powerful weight, the shapely, sculptured hands that were flying about.

'Don't try to deceive me,' Rosa said oddly, with a kind of terrible accusation lurking in her jetty eyes.

'I haven't known you long enough for that. It might have been better had you gone off to bed,' Frances suggested, dying to escape this dreary, disgusting scene. And *what* was it all about?

Rosa suddenly struck herself on her handsome breast, an infuriated, utterly helpless gesture that made Frances, even in the midst of it, feel sorry for her. 'Why are you so angry?' she asked reasonably. 'What do you imagine might happen?'

'Whatever it is I am the one who will suffer for it,' Rosa hurled at her, making Frances wonder if she was perhaps losing her mind. With feigned self-possession she moved away from the door. 'I might remind you, Rosa, while you're breathing maternal fire all over me, that this is my grandfather's house and I'm a guest in it. So far as I'm aware, I've done nothing wrong, nothing to cause your anger and resentment. It's quite inexplicable to me. Dario is old enough to get home under his own steam. So am I. And while we're on the subject, you can keep your charming comments about David Sutherland to yourself. So far as I'm concerned you're dead wrong!'

'*Si, si,* I know. How dare you speak to me with your heartless Donovan tongue!' Rosa shouted, her black eyes burning feverishly.

'Oh, don't be absurd!' Frances stared at her wearily. 'My own mother wouldn't dream of bailing me up in this ridiculous fashion, so why on earth should I put up with it from you? You seem to be accusing me of something and I can't for the life of me think what it is. Dario's twenty-five. He's a big boy now. Perhaps he's enjoying himself with Madellana Rossi. Then, I take it, you'd be all smiles.'

Rosa gave a little gloating laugh full of triumph. 'Madellana is a pious, sensible girl who allows herself to be directed. She comes from a good Italian family. I know them, I have stayed in their home. They are my dear friends—and I have precious few of them, thanks to your dear grandfather. Madellana has been taught from earliest childhood to cherish and obey her elders and betters.'

'Poor thing!' Frances said with an abstracted touch of mockery. 'She could do with a bit of updating—and not only in the way she dresses.'

Rosa went scarlet in the face with embarrassment. 'Madellana Rossi is worth a dozen of such young women as you!' she said loyally.

'*Make* a dozen, you mean,' Frances was driven on ridiculously. 'She's overweight all ready. You must have read all the latest information, Rosa. Add inches to your waistline and you'll only take years off your lifeline.' She broke off, impatient and disgusted with herself. 'I don't know why I'm attacking poor Madellana. She seemed a nice, hostile girl.'

Rosa's wild laugh was indescribable. 'You ... you ... would let another woman take your man from you?'

'If I had to fight for his attention I certainly would. That's the way I am.'

'What could you know of it?' Rosa cried.

'I know myself. Pride runs in the family.'

Rosa broke into torrential Italian, none of which was flattering to the Donovans. 'It does indeed,' she said bitterly, sobering. 'Not a characteristic to be proud of. Your grandfather now ...' she went on in her least attractive tone.

'Yes, Rosa, continue.'

'You're awake, Grandfather!' '... *No!*' Both women pronounced their words together.

Vincent Donovan was standing in the doorway in an attitude of heavy attention and authority. Pyjamas, a silk robe and felt slippers did nothing to detract from the living strength of his personality. 'How could I be otherwise, with this clash of angry voices?'

'I'm sorry, Grandfather, I didn't realise,' Frances apologised, thinking how foolish Rosa had been to precipitate such a scene. 'Shall I take you back to bed?'

'Thank you, no. Where is Desmond?'

'Putting the car away,' Frances lied, seeing Rosa appeared to be caught up in a speechless ecstasy like a Michelangelo sculpture.

The glance Vincent Donovan gave her would have been eloquent in any language. 'Kindly don't lie to me, Fran, though I realise it's your kind heart that inspires you. It seems my grandson has not seen fit to escort his cousin home. We shall go into the drawing room and wait for him—however long that will take. You, Rosa, get more than enough rest and Frances is young enough to go without.'

Rosa rolled her great agonised eyes around and Frances hurried into an explanation. 'David Sutherland offered to drive me home, Grandfather. It was really my fault I came on without Dario. He was enjoying himself so much and I was a little tired. It didn't seem fair to bring him away. David offered—and there you are. No harm done at all. Surely you understand?'

'I do not, and pray don't continue to defend your cousin. Desmond is the greatest possible disappointment to me, in every way. He has failed in his responsibilities to me and the family interests since long before his father died. He has failed his mother too, and she him—the too soft woman's hand, foolish indulgence. I don't intend that this state of affairs should continue. I will not have all I've striven for in a lifetime pass into wastrel hands.'

'Oh, Grandfather!' Frances said, shocked by his hardness. Dario was no wastrel. A little lazy about things that didn't matter a great deal to him perhaps, but Dario had heart, great sensibility. Rosa the voluble was pitifully silent. She must be raging inwardly to hear her son so maligned. The evening was mounting to a nightmare climax. Inexplicably Frances wanted Scot Sutherland there. He would always provide a balance, cut through to the real core of the matter. Pity Dario when he did arrive!

Suddenly the front door opened and Dario stepped forward into the light, the creative pleasure that had so washed over him in an overwhelming flood ludicrously abated by the sight of the faces turned to him—his mother despairing, Francesca with 'togetherness' written all over her, his grandfather, policeman and judge. Thank God he wasn't drunk again. When he had entered the place was very quiet; now his grandfather's voice rang out harshly.

'In here, Desmond, if you don't mind.'

Something rose up in him, for the first time in all his adult life—revolt. His mother's desperation was reaching him in great waves. He walked into the drawing room feeling the atmosphere. One thing was certain—they weren't banded together. Frances came forward in her flying leaf fashion to grasp his arm. Dario relaxed a little and smiled into her lovely, passionate young face. 'What is it, *cara*? What's happening? I'm so sorry we missed one another, but wait until you see what I have for you.'

'We'll deal with that later,' his grandfather said with steely savagery, with the fixed belief in his mind that his grandson Desmond was a capricious drop-out with no sense of duty. The moment had a dreamlike strangeness yet a bitter familiarity. Ghosts of other days. His sons, the mercurial Robert and the incredibly near, nearly twenty-year-old tragedy. Stored-up grief gave him an old man's violence and he launched into a bitter tirade that Rosa had learnt to accept with weary resignation and Dario had fortunately not paid a great deal of attention to.

'Grandfather, *please*!' Frances tried to stop the powerful flow. Vincent Donovan's hard, gaunt face looked terrible. She had been standing, ranged, alongside Dario, but now she crossed to the old man's side. He was standing there, killing himself, raging to the bitter end. 'You can't mean all you're saying. I won't believe it!'

'Things never change!' the old man said with cruel irony. He was breathing very fast, high unaccustomed colour on his cheekbones.

'This is all my fault,' she said, distressed beyond belief. What had Dario ever done to deserve all that? 'Dario is an artist, a fine one. Can't you see that, Grandfather? He's not a farmer and no one can make him one.'

'We'll see about that!' Vincent Donovan replied. 'Why in God's name do you defend him, girl? You have spirit, courage, determination. What has he got? Talent, you tell me. I've seen no sign of it. Only his mother's unspeaking enmity. They're both of them waiting for me to die.'

'Grandfather, please don't say any more,' she entreated him, her amber eyes filling with tears.

He muttered a little madly to himself and put out his hand to her with a convulsive gesture. 'What good will he ever be if you don't make something out of him?'

'Oh, *please*!' she said again, more frantically, feeling she was being driven into a corner. 'I'm going to take you along to bed, Grandfather, you've upset yourself dreadfully—and for what?'

'A damned gigolo,' he said in a tortured tone. 'A creature who hides behind a woman's skirts.'

'You do Dario a great injustice,' Frances said with sad emphasis. 'You're an old man, Grandfather. Dario with his fine sensibility simply couldn't yield to the desire to retaliate.'

'You think so, girl? Take me to bed.' The old man's movements were jerky, but Rosa's stony face did not soften. It said a great deal for her terrific self-control that she had not throttled her father-in-law as she had often wanted to. He beat everyone into pulp in the end.

Dario was thrusting his fingers through his hair. His face was very pale, but he didn't say a word. After a moment his mother got up and cradled his head against her. 'Why do we stand it, why?' she moaned.

'He's not always like this,' Dario supplied. 'I beg of you, Mamma, let's go away. We don't need the money.'

'Fool! Foolish boy! We do need the money. I've not worked all these long years for nothing. Your father slaved, killed himself to make this farm one of the most prosperous in the state. My happiness died in the wink of an eye, and you talk about leaving! I tell you, my son, I'll see that old man out. I'll contest his will, if it comes to that.'

'Oh, Mamma, all this is deplorable!' Dario passed a hand over his thick curls. 'Poor little Francesca, did you see her? Her compassionate little face revealed so perfectly her own happy home life.'

'That one!' Rosa grunted painfully, her cold hand clasping her son's.

'Don't speak like that, Mamma, I won't have it!' Dario resisted her touch. 'Francesca knows a great deal about loving, lucky girl. Then too, she has a loving heart herself. Neither of us can afford to do without it.'

'She knows what she's doing!' Rosa persisted carefully.

'Defending me, mostly,' Dario muttered, not without humour.

'For a purpose!'

'Oh, stop it! I *know* Francesca. What she is is reflected in her eyes. She's so small, yet so gallant she almost makes me cry. The extraordinary part is she really cares about that terrible old man. Someone in this whole wide world really cares about Vincent Donovan. I don't think that's been done before, not even by his mother. Still, he's made a great impression on us all. Some men just have to have power—wealth or personality, or both, to triumph over people. They're ruthless and they just don't care, but ironically enough there's always someone to care about them. Why don't we make a new life for ourselves, Mamma, stand on our own two feet? Four feet, actually. We should be able to make it. Francesca would tell me I haven't the guts!'

'*Guts!*' his mother roared as if a red-hot poker was pressed to her breast. 'What do you know about it? Me, I have it and more. For God's sake, Dario, do you think I'll allow anyone to take your inheritance from you? Your father didn't die an early death so you could go without. I have put up with this lousy half-life all for you, nobody else. I am a woman of passion, should you spare me a glance. I could have married again, had more children. But no, my whole life since your father died has been a sublimation—all for you. Your grandfather is a very rich man, and what do we, his family, have? Nothing. *Nulla!'* She flung her hands extravagantly in the air. 'I've lived with it, slept with it, brooded over it . . .'

'And become tainted with it, perhaps, Mamma. We should have gone long ago, like Francesca's mother. She must have had courage. Grandfather doesn't see me as his true grandson, I've always known that. I have too much Adami in me, thank God!' Dario looked down at the thick pad he had thrown on the desk and patted it painfully. 'And my dear father too. I have his talent.'

'You're brushed with genius, my son,' said Rosa, clutching his collarbone, her black eyes glittering venom for Vincent Donovan, 'but as your mother with far more common sense, I must make the decisions. You will not throw your inheritance away for some grand gesture. I'm not giving up now. Some day soon the old man will die—I've hoped it a dozen times before tonight.'

'Mamma, Mamma!' Dario covered his ears desperately, and even Rosa stopped, exhausted by her own quivering passions. Such brutal things the old man had said of his grandson—and in front of *her*, the usurper with her red hair and cat's eyes. She was all Donovan. It was true the old man had never accepted Dario, even as an infant and so beautiful and engaging. This girl, this Francesca, who had appeared out of nowhere, could not hope to be his legitimate heir. That would be so grossly unfair as to be insupportable. She, Rosa, had not spent all these long years cooking and washing and caring for the old man for absolutely nothing! She fumed inwardly now, stroking Dario's smooth nape, the thunderous pressure of blood in her veins.

Her unspeaking enmity! He was right about that—and enmity for a very good reason. She would never of herself been like that. Once in the very early days she had sincerely tried to love him for Desmond's sake, but *non posso*. Her womanhood was gone, over, when her man had never come back from the canefields. No miracle on earth could put that right again, but she could save something for her son—a mountain of money. Forget the grand gestures, the idealism. One could well do without them, but not the money. Vulgar it might be, but it was the magic formula. For Dario it would open every door, set free her chained spirit.

Francesca, coming back into the room, instantly perceived Rosa's dreams and the scorn and hostility, but Dario lifted his head, his dark eyes soft, smiling at her gratefully. Those large, lustrous eyes were filled with affection—no, more than that, love. In some way already, Dario loved her. Pray God it was only familial love that coloured her own attitude towards him. Dario aroused her protective streak as he would in many another woman, but not, she thought, the bright light of sexual attraction. Yet why the certitude? Dario was a very attractive young man, in fact he was as strikingly picturesque as Rosa, his mother. He was nothing like that monster of attraction Scot Sutherland. That was a hard, deliberate charm, a stinging high-handedness and a sensual technique that must have owed at least something to a great deal of practice. Dario was different, gentle. He needed protection. Grandfather's unjustifiable tirade had only desperately intensified Frances' feeling for her cousin. That Grandfather had done this sort of thing often was apparent from the look of bitter anguish and unrelenting antagonism on Rosa's sculptured face, with its fine nose and full, slightly quivering lips.

Rosa had had a raw deal from life, Frances considered, and as she thought this, her expression softened as she looked across at the older woman.

'Shall I get you something, Rosa? You look very pale. A little brandy?'

'Thank you, *nothing*!' Rosa declared, not mollified. Rosa was a fortress to be besieged in vain, or perhaps more graphically, a Delacroix sketch of a mother lion defending her cub. Beneath that thick creamy olive skin flowed the violent and furious blood. Rosa was certainly memorable, as steely in her fashion as ever Grandfather could be, and he tucked up in his bed equally fierce, as spare and angular as only the old can be.

About Dario now was an unexpected look of intense preoccupation, a lynx-eyed observation. The black eyes shone with an electric kind of brilliance that was all the more remarkable considering the distressing scene that had gone before. But Dario was seized by the whole idea of action and luminous effects. Those pirouettes of Francesca's had set him off—soaring *grands jetés* and graceful arabesques. He was no Dégas, but he had considerable skill with rapid techniques. The innumerable pencil sketches he had done tonight bore that out. Family arguments, complex and hotly passionate, fell away from him, forgotten. Dario was safely cocooned in a world that was fast taking him over: Francesca as a model, the great impetus. She positively pulsated with life, colour, movement. She was a born dancer—he should have guessed that from her lovely way of moving, the chic and the poise long years of training had lent her, a flying leaf in the wind. He leaned forward and threw open the heavy pad covered in chains of sketches.

Frances came to his side to exclaim with absolute

sincerity: 'Why, Dario, what an elegant craftsman you are! These are beautiful, show me——' Sweetly imperious, she took the pad from his hand, slowly turning the pages. 'You should have used pastel, then you would have been able to get colour into them as well.'

'None to hand,' Dario supplied, well pleased with her spontaneous opinion. 'These were done tonight, locked away in Dave's gunroom. Plenty of guns, but no pastels, alas!'

'Beautiful!' Frances said again reverently. 'They're even recognisably me!' Her fingers strayed to his glossy curls, tweaking them with affection. She was pleased and proud of him, almost in the same wonderful way of mothers, but neither Rosa nor Dario saw this. Dario was finding her exquisitely appealing, while Rosa was seeing her ambitions thwarted in their fulfilment. Even at a glance the drawings were splendid—construction, texture, light and shade, all presented with a masterly young hand. Simplicity itself, seemingly, but great detail had been paid to anatomical form. All sorts of classical ballet poses were expressed, model's head and limbs thrown back or forwards, muscles indicated, the lovely curve of the breast, the slight swell of the ribcage as the body was tilted back off centre. It was very easy to visualise that beautifully shaped body which she didn't really think of as hers, beneath the filmy draperies—and there too, the very substance of the thin chiffon had been faithfully represented. Veils of soft gossamer. Oh, he was clever!

'Pianists have a piano, dancers have their own body!' Dario pronounced. 'Don't be ashamed of it, cara, it's so supple and pliant.'

'I'm not, you know,' she said lightly. 'I trained

long enough—eight long years until I was seven-teen. It was once suggested to me as a career, but the life is too restricting, very hard and demanding, and aching feet at the end of each day. Only the dance and plain indifference to everything else. I haven't got it in me.'

'Well, the lyrical movement is there. You're an inspiration, little one—and such a beautifully shaped body.'

'And these are a lovely tribute to me. Thank you, Dario, I'm honoured.'

'You should be!' Rosa pointed out sharply in a jealous outrage. No other woman had ever chal-lenged her position as the most important woman in Dario's young life. Madellana would make an excellent wife and mother, but not *that*! Mothers were born in heaven, wives not at all. This girl oc-cupied no such position. Still, she could have her uses. Every artist required a motivating force, fresh stimulus. It might be wise in this one instance not to interfere. Wasn't it enough to see Dario lose that stricken look, the misery around the eyes and mouth, too deep for bitterness—but then the sweet-ness and generosity of Dario's nature made bitter-ness difficult. So completely was he obsessed by his vision, even his grandfather's black wash of vindic-tiveness couldn't penetrate his concentration. Such a miracle!

Rosa didn't mean it, but when she found her voice it was like dark run honey and vaguely self-reproachful. 'Come, Francesca, let us go to our beds and forget the awful aftermath of such a happy evening. This must be very embarrassing for you. Don't think for one moment that I don't feel for you, my dear. I am terribly sorry, but now it is over. Dario and I have lived through many such incidents. That is the whole thing about your grandfather. He has always been like this, as I'm sure your own mother would tell you. We mustn't let it affect us but proceed with our lives, regardless!'

The swish of her heavy silken robe filled the room as she bent over her son, murmuring a passionately, maternal benediction:

'Goodnight, my dearest son, my beloved!'

Dario pressed a muffled kiss into her breast, already half way out of her reach. 'Goodnight, Mamma!'

In her statuesque fashion Rosa moved towards the frozen Frances, laying strong fingers on her arm, a fine blaze in the depths of her black eyes. 'We will leave my son to his own private world. It is very late, I know, but the great thing is, he is happy. That means everything to me!'

'It means a great deal to me too, Rosa,' Frances said, forcing her voice to control.

'Then we are one,' Rosa said grandly. 'We ought to thank God for it!'

But she didn't, of course. Frances had a swift grasp of that. Rosa wouldn't consider handing over the reins of her destiny to another. She might go to church every Sunday, she might think and speak of herself as a deeply religious woman, but she felt perfectly capable of looking after herself. To call on heaven was overdoing the melodrama.

Frances let Rosa guide her to the door. She longed for escape, but briefly searched her mind for the reason for Rosa's volte-face which instinct told her was forced. The effects of the evening had taken their toll. It was sunrise before her body and mind had settled enough for her to sleep.

Sunday promised to be quite dreadful if neither Vincent Donovan nor his daughter-in-law were determined to yield an inch. There was no question in Frances' mind that the family could sit down together for the midday meal without some kind of blackhearted skirmish. Such a state of affairs was calculated to send the best woman back to her bed. She was a little pale and tired after her own restless night, though she did not show it much, but she dreaded even the thought of laying the table. The only diplomatic thing to do was to prepare a light tray for her grandfather and take it along to him. For once he hadn't bothered with the morning ritual of shower and shave and freshly laundered clothes. He was lying in his bed amid the morning papers looking haggard and easily provoked, right out of sorts—and with her as well. His greeting was tart, but he held up his face, and Frances put down the tray on the table by his bed and bent to kiss the paper-dry cheek.

Vincent Donovan watched her sardonically. He was cheered more than he could ever admit or express by her presence. He was even jealous in his way of her spirited defence of her cousin and the way she had taken him to task last night before settling him for the night as if he were no more than a terrible child out of joint with the world. He admired her for her loyalty and it suited his purpose well, but it irritated him rather badly. He couldn't have borne another grandchild like Desmond, not at any price. No one had even seen fit to fly to his defence—not that he had ever needed help from anyone. Just as well, with two sons dead and the others dependent on him, but not little Fran. She was a true Donovan—no dreamy drawer, but a doer, a worker, and as spunky as she had been as a child. She would hold and make prosper all that he had so painfully won, and not a one of them willing to give him credit for the long, long years of back-breaking hard work. Daylight right into the dark and seven days a week, with none of your holidays and sick leave and tea-breaks and all the rest. Just plenty of hard work, and how he had thrived on it! Won a security few men in these parts attained to, and there were plenty comfortably off. He was worth a great deal more than anyone supposed. Not a soul in the town knew about those mineral shares, for instance. Real estate, yes, he couldn't hide that.

It would all go to Fran, he could see that now. She had been sent to him, sent to make something of Desmond, who after all had his own blood, though it was damned difficult to see any visible sign of it. Sometimes, though, the gentle, musing look reminded him of Ellen, his wife, who had simply faded away with no fight at all. Frances was a fighter. It was written all over her. She would take Desmond in hand. His mother, Rosa, had ruined him, pandering to a wishy-washy talent. Drawing, bah! Any girl could do that. Why, he could draw well enough himself if it came to that.

There was nothing his son Desmond couldn't have brought to life on paper, but Desmond had known what was really important in life—the farm, Sugar Hill, the family interests, all the time moving up in the world. Already the boy was under Fran's spell, as any young man in his senses would be. He had set aside a paltry legacy, by his standards, for his living daughter-in-law Rosa. He couldn't afford to be stingy to his own memory, otherwise she could go without. When he felt stronger he would have a serious chat with young

Fran. It had taken him long enough to get where he was. He wasn't going to let Desmond drag them down again. Only last week he had found some of the young cane with leaf burn. Of course it was due to that dry, windy patch, but Desmond hadn't even noticed, with broad, dead streaks right up the full width of the leaf blade. Young fool!

'Feeling better, darling?' Frances enquired gently, seeing the hot words that were trembling on the old man's tongue.

'No thanks to that wretched family of mine,' Vincent Donovan said maliciously, waving his spoon about.

'Now listen to me, Grandad,' Frances said sternly. 'You're not going to start off upsetting yourself. Last night was my fault, I thought I explained that, and now we're going to forget it, otherwise I'll catch the first plane home. We've all got a roof over our heads, a beautiful home and property, the weather couldn't be better, something nice to eat—I prepared that tray myself—so we don't have a thing to worry about.'

'And I think you're a fool to bother about your cousin,' Vincent Donovan said with affectionate disgust.

'Now, now, Grandfather!' Frances said reprovingly, her young voice somehow seasoned with love. 'Would you like me to sit with you a while?'

'Yes!' Vincent Donovan barked. 'Read me the papers—I don't seem to be able to hold them straight. Sit over there in the sun, then I can see the lights in your hair,' he said simply. 'You're a beautiful girl, Fran, I suppose you know that. When you were little you used to call me Poppy in such a piping voice, like a small bird. *Poppy!*' he mused, sadly reflective.

'And I'll call you Poppy again. I'm no different now from what I was then. I love you, Granddad.'

'Yes, I know,' Vincent Donovan said gently. 'The only one who has never resented my authority. Where did I go wrong, Fran?' For a moment the hardness, the singlemindedness, the ruthless determination fell away from him and he was only an increasingly frail old man who looked suddenly, unendurably humble.

'Don't fret, Granddad,' she said quickly, her amber eyes fond. 'You're a most remarkable man, though unmistakably a terror! One can't have everything. I suppose you were so busy making your fortune you forget about everyone else.'

'I had time enough for you,' her grandfather grunted waspishly.

'So you had! Which just goes to show what good taste you've got. Now, just listen to this . . .' She broke off, skimming her finger down the printed page of the paper. 'What about this column, an old pal of yours!' She began to read an article about a well-known politician and her grandfather laughed heartily.

'And about time too!' he said unjustly, with an expression of satisfaction on his face. 'Put him in power and the whole lot of us are heading for disaster. Pettish, my God!' Rosa and Desmond were forgotten. He had his granddaughter by his side and she shared his humour. Because he was honest, Vincent Donovan admitted that it was wrong, but alone of all his children and their children, he loved her, little Fran. A natural phenomenon, perhaps.

The broad strong hand on the quilt that had been twitching from time to time uncontrollably relaxed. The vein in the temple stopped throbbing. He sipped his tea gratefully, listening to that golden young voice skipping to this and that article, making jokes. Yes, Fran would look after him. Those wide amber eyes said: trust me! Frances didn't stand in awe of him. She wasn't afraid of him. She loved him—the first and only time in his life. Frances alone would mourn him. He knew that, for he was coming near to the end of his life. He didn't care. He was old and tired now. He didn't feel himself any more. A man in his eighties had lived long enough. But first he had to settle the family affairs.

CHAPTER SIX

It was very hot and still in the garden, a rather tormented Sunday afternoon. Frances lay in the hammock, a book in her restless hands, the sweetness of frangipanni and wild honeysuckle in her nostrils. She felt anything but lethargic in the seductive heat, her hair framing her face in dark flame-coloured tendrils, curling out on to her honey skin. A scarlet poinciana blossom descended on to her face and she brushed it off. Soon she would have to do something or go mad. Dario, far from snapping out of his creative mood, was more deeply immersed in it and Rosa had kept to her room with its private court for the best part of the day.

She would take the car for a run, Frances decided. She would like to 'have a go' at the Rolls. It would be fun, but she had the hundred per cent correct notion that Grandfather wouldn't allow it. Now, what was this book about? A thriller-romance. She had read page forty-four at least a dozen times. She struggled with the top line ... 'I didn't kill her, though I tried damned hard to make her give me the diamonds!' Good grief! Normally, that would have gripped her attention; now it was all she could do not to yawn. Disappointing for the author, one of her favourites.

She shut her eyes, unwilling to wrestle with the rest. She would find out what happened to the diamonds later. She already knew who had done the murder. Abruptly into her mind came a hard, handsome face, every lean, chiselled feature in minutest detail. What a thing! A devilish twist for the afternoon. Purposefully she tried to drain her mind blank. Her all-important need was simple: to relax. There would be none of that if she started thinking about David Sutherland. Not in the shadowy beauty of a tropical garden, hushed and scented, the sun slanting in soft beams through the fretwork of trees. It was all so frankly sensuous, like a Gauguin painting. Frances stirred a little restlessly, drawing up her long legs, a frown between the lovely pencilled line of her brows and lashes.

Some little time later a car purred up the drive. A tall figure stepped out and made for the veranda stairs. For some reason the man turned his dark head and saw her away in the garden. Immediately he changed direction and struck across the grass, making straight for her. His long shadow fell across her and his warm, vibrant fingers took the book from her hands. He glanced at it idly, laughed, and put it aside.

'What a sad fate for a heroine, to be murdered—

and not a very clever murder at that! Wake up, Frances Donovan, or I'll tweak your hair.'

'I *am* awake!' she announced, her voice cracking a little, not only with surprise. Something like a bonfire had just shot through her veins.

'I know,' he said lightly, his eyes on her face and down her slight body. 'Fluttery eyelashes, however fabulous, are a dead give-away. Where's everyone?' He turned his head towards the house, giving his rare, very attractive smile, a smile that conveyed so much more than his words did.

'Sleeping, I think,' she said, trying to be casual. 'A typical Sunday afternoon siesta.'

'Dario *sleeping*?' he flashed her a look of brilliant disbelief. 'Not with you outside, *cara!*' His hand came out and tucked a thick strand of hair behind her ear. 'Miss me?'

'I hadn't got as far as that.'

'What a pity!'

'Besides,' she continued artlessly, 'I don't go around with signs on me.'

'Oh? I thought you did.' His voice was threaded with cynical amusement, his shimmery eyes like diamond chips. All diamonds this afternoon. Briefly they touched her face, her throat, her breast, the taut, narrow hips, her long lovely legs. 'I don't actually like to see you like this, Francesca, on a long, hot afternoon.'

'Thank you!' she said, trying to be sarcastic, but it came out faintly husky, that was all.

'Shall I go away?'

'Oh *no!*' She couldn't help that and she felt the shock of her own betrayal colouring her face.

'Then come for a drive with me. I'll take you back to the house. You can explore it if you like—I think you'd like to do that. Then if you're especially good I'll show you the best of my horses. You put me in mind of a special favourite of mine, an excitable bright chestnut!'

'I'd like that,' she said quickly, gripped by the curious intimacy of the moment. 'Dario might like to come.'

'I said *you*!'

'In any case he's busy,' Frances smiled, inordinately pleased with that emphatic *you*. Small even white teeth against a pomegranate mouth. 'I've an idea Dario intends painting me.'

'Good. You're eminently paintable,' Scot agreed casually. 'Had I the talent I'd paint you myself.'

Tremors of an uneasy excitement were thrilling through her veins. He was looking at her in that way again. No one had ever looked at her like that. She could feel her heart begin to pound, but she could only lie there feeling so vulnerable. She should be standing up, full of fight, yet she couldn't help her eyes fluttering to his mouth.

'Habit-forming!' he said, and the words burned like acid.

'What?'

'Kissing some women, You start out with one peck and pretty soon you can't think of anything else.'

'Not *you*?' she said hardily.

'Not yet! Get up, Frances Donovan.' He put out his hands and cupped her slender waist, lifting her in one effortless glide to the ground. It seemed to be shaking as if from a recent earthquake.

In a flurry she bent her head, searching the ground for her sandals. The bright silky hair fell away from her tender young nape and he ran his finger across it and into the soft hollow at the side of her neck. She trembled violently and swung her head up to face him with a quick look of challenge, a don't-touch-me-or-else!

'Poor cat,' he gave a faint smile, his silvery eyes narrowing to slits. 'On the defensive and she doesn't know why!'

'I know why, all right,' she said tautly. 'I could never completely trust you, David Sutherland.'

'Wise girl! I don't even mind that you're one of the few people who doesn't call me Scot. Here are your sandals. Are you coming or not, because if you are you'll have to change. I've no objection to a bit of a halter and shorts, but you might upset some of my staff. You're amazingly eye-catching!'

'In that case, I'll put on a dress. Something long!'

'It would help!' There was something not quite a smile in his eyes, as if he rather wished she was not quite so attractive. 'Is your grandfather about? I'd like a word with him.'

For some reason her forehead broke out in a cold sweat. 'David . . .' she said, and hesitated, her hand, without volition, going out to him. Nameless anxieties were there in her amber eyes, and his own eyes sharpened.

'What is it? What's wrong at the house?'

'There was rather an argument last night.'

'Hell!' He gripped her shoulder to spin her round to him, almost hurting her. 'Why didn't you tell me before?'

'Oh, really, David, there's a limit on what one is supposed to tell, and you know we're not exactly friends. Would you wait for me here?'

'If that's how you want it,' he said without enthusiasm. 'I won't pretend it's not what I'm used to nor what I want.'

'I realise that!' she said sharply as if he had

flicked at her with a whip. 'Patrice would have been opening up drinks. Champagne, I suppose, with *Scot* around.'

'Jealous?'

'You're crazy!' The light glanced oddly across her triangular face, the honey-gold skin and the gleaming amber eyes, a rosy, softly burning mouth.

'You look more a witch now!' he said in a voice that made the blood pound in her head.

'It helps at times. I could put an outsize spell on you.'

'You'd never frighten me,' he said lazily. 'You didn't really think you could, did you, Frances? You like to think of yourself as a proper little caution, all that bright air of independence, but you're only a kitten at heart!'

She stepped on to a high flat rock the better to get on level with him and he laughed outright— not a very kind laugh. 'I didn't say you couldn't provoke me, as you'll find out if you care to stand around!'

'Oh, I see!' She didn't realise it, but her eyes looked almost desperate. She tossed her bright head and tilted her pointed chin. Those incandescent eyes troubled her, that arrogant air. Anyone would think that he owned her! 'I won't be long,' she said, feigning a pleasant tone, when she could have strangled him.

'I'll be here!' he said, unexpectedly gentle, seeing beneath the youthful hostility, a hidden excitement.

She gazed back at him, trying to fathom the look on his dark face.

'Hurry up, idiot child.'

'Always so masterful!'

'So Patrice says.'

Her breath came in a soft gasp and she turned and fled with her curious, fluid elegance, one part of her mind given over to what she should wear. In the end she settled for burnt gold slacks and a printed shirt blooming with outsize chrysanthemums. It would, at least, be practical. She wanted to explore that beautiful bush garden. Bush gardens were something else again; no mowing, no maintenance, no weeding, just a close harmony with the natural environment. Australia boasted extraordinarily prolific native flora with a greater variety in the Sydney area alone than in the whole of the British Isles. The Sutherland place should be really worth seeing. There had been no chance last night at the party, but Frances had overheard Patrice in a rave over David's—or Scot's, rather—. in that drawly, affected voice, landscape artist. Hastily she penned out a note for the family and left it on the dining room table, a tactful expect-me-when-you-see-me.

In reality the garden was even more beautiful than she had imagined, as she was soon to find out. A luxurious thick carpet of fallen leaves and purplish bracken, the beauty of casuarina needles, and bent over them, a canopy of flowering eucalypts and wattles, the graceful melaleucas and the fantastic banksias with their odd little nut men perched along the branches. Different types of ground cover were everywhere she looked, dwarf prickly mosses and lichens and all types of ferns: tiny terrestrial orchids and native violets, blue and lilac and often pure white, a trailing ivy with yellow flowers and the gold and white everlasting daisies. There were wonderful boulders and great spherical clumps of silver and pink pampas grass. Frances looked and Scot strolled by her side.

They were following a path of raked sand that twisted in and out of a tea tree copse sown with flannel flowers and the dog rose, lovely pieces of driftwood he must have brought from the coast. The water garden was closer to the house in a quiet haven of leafy shade with purple flag and blue waterlilies, little necklace and water ferns and lovely young bottlebrushes with their pink tips of new growth. Frances bent down and picked up a handful of pearl-white pebbles.

'They're beautiful, aren't they? They feel so satisfying.'

'Yes.' He took some from her palm, fingering them over. 'We've learned a great deal from the Orient there. I like the look of stones and pebbles in the garden, as you can see. Water-washed creek stones. The big boulders I had shifted to the site. Expensive but well worth it, I think.'

'Who was your landscape artist?'

'You're joking!' One black eyebrow shot up. 'Geoffrey and I worked this out on paper at first. It wasn't difficult. I've any amount of ground. A small suburban lot would have been far more of a challenge. Why ever would you imagine I'd need a landscape artist?'

'Oh, I thought you had one. Just a chance remark I overheard last night.'

'Well, obviously whoever made it doesn't know me that well!' he said carelessly. 'You can feel the warmth in these stones. They absorb the hot sun and keep the roots of all these little plants moist.'

'When would a woman be asked to share all this?' she asked rather impishly, perched precariously on a fallen limb, shaking back her bright hair.

'Are you offering?'

'Heavens, no! What a mind-boggling thought, Mr Sutherland. Besides, I'm sure I wouldn't qualify.'

'That's certainly right!'

'Cad!' she said reproachfully, when she had asked for it.

'But that doesn't mean you're entirely out of danger.'

'Oh?' Her face turned as rosy as a flower, but he only strolled nonchalantly towards her.

'Why, with another five or six years on you, young Frances, you just might turn out all right.'

'Thank you! You're certainly one for the compliments. Short, straight and deadly.'

'And you've been spoiled. You expect instant adoration and I can't find it in me. I feel a little towards you as I would towards a fantastically pretty, quite contrary child.'

'And you feel nothing else?' she asked, for some reason tantalisingly sure of herself, and apparently all for nothing.

A look of intense amusement hovered around his mouth. 'I've decided, Francesca, not to tell you.'

'And I don't want to know!'

'Then why tilt your chin like that? An air of challenge can be infuriating in a woman.'

'And how perfectly you sound like a *man*!'

'It would be comical if I didn't!' he said mildly, a silvery warning light in those uncanny irises. 'This conversation wouldn't be taking place otherwise. The thing is, young Frances, there's a single fatal flaw in the set-up. I've always had an irremediable passion for redheads!'

'Cured now, I feel sure.'

'I wouldn't say that.'

She moved quickly. 'If you're quite finished teasing me, may I look at the house? It's exhausting doing battle with your kind of man.'

'Please tell me what kind is that?'

She hadn't reckoned on his look of subtle sex antagonism, as alarming as it was attractive. 'A d-d-damned, high-handed autocrat,' she said, stuttering, and taking to her heels. 'Frankly I don't like it, but I love your house.'

He cut her off easily and she pulled away from him, breathless, stars bursting softly in front of her eyes. 'Oh, please, I didn't mean it!' she said with a frantic little tremble of entreaty.

'They why try me out? Lift your head, there's nothing to be afraid of!'

'Let me decide that.' Her heavy silk hair shielded her face.

'What kind of a man am I?' he repeated, shaking her gently.

'Give me time to think about it.'

'You might refuse to tell me if I ask you later on.'

She ran the tip of her tongue over her quivering mouth and risked lifting her head. 'I'm sure I'll *love* you when I get to know you better. How's that?'

'Well worth waiting for,' he said laconically. 'You'd love me for myself, Francesca, not because I'm one of the richest men around here.'

'I know nothing about that!' she said, shocked by the hard note in his voice, the dangerous line between his winged brows.

'Look around you, little one.'

'Well, it doesn't interest me,' she said emphatically, 'beyond a very natural appreciation of beautiful surroundings. I don't envy you anything, Mr Sutherland! Neither do I want anything from you, except perhaps a cup of coffee.'

'All right, all right, I believe you!' he said, suddenly relenting, his thumb caressing the line of her neck—an involuntary action, it seemed, for he was looking into his own mind, his eyes almost glacial with memories. 'One gets a little cynical after a while, but that's a long story.'

'I shouldn't think you'd have to worry,' she said heatedly. 'You're too damned attractive by far!'

He came right back to the present, giving a low burst of laughter. 'Why, Frances, what an admission! Were I not so set against marriage I'd fall entirely under your spell of enchantment.'

'Oh damn!' she said, her sweet young voice sounding strangled.

'No, really, Frances!' he said, still laughing and pulling her hard up against him. 'Dario is not the only man to thirst after beauty. Face flushed and eyes luminous—I have to admit you just could be intoxicating, but I'm no glutton for punishment. Women can be very destructive, stupid and cruel, killing a man's vision and initiative utterly!'

'Oh, but that's monstrous!'

He caught her face with his hand and she put up her own hand to stay it. 'What about all the vicious, selfish men in the world? The drunkards and gamblers, the men who make their wives and families suffer. If you weren't so damned cynical as you say, and why I don't know, you'd acknowledge that some women bring glory to a man's life. Have you ever thought of that?'

'I've thought of it, certainly,' he admitted with a drawl, 'but I've never actually seen it. I have seen plenty of slaves!'

'Oh, really! Why. . . .'

He bent and kissed her protesting mouth hard. 'I

could listen to your passionate eloquence all day, Frances, but for one thing, I value my peace of mind. Besides, you've a mouth that's framed better for making love.'

'You fiend! Men like to act pontifical and then walk away.'

'You're absolutely right! The one thing I don't want from you is an argument.'

Her amber eyes flashed, all her attention focused on his hard, handsome face. Very oddly indeed, his shimmery eyes held a quality of ... was it *tenderness*? Fantastic—it couldn't be. Frances knew in her bones that he was antagonistic to her. Her young face was uplifted, full of a strange purity and passion, the sun on it like a blazing net of magic or a spotlight on a stage.

'Women for centuries have been conquered and possessed,' she said, trying to stop trembling, 'but not any more! It's about time we women got square. We have the right to be ourselves, to live and to work and to follow the dictates of our own natures, not live in the shadow of a man's experience!'

'Go on,' he said gently. 'I'm utterly absorbed. I can see this is a theme you really care about.'

'I do!'

'You've won my esteem at any rate. I feel like a man who's struck on buried treasure!'

'Ridicule is no argument!' she said passionately, his hand like a sword on her collarbone.

'I apologise. Speak on, Francesca, with your quenchless abandon, the innocence of youth burning brightly. I value your opinion.'

'You *don't*, so I won't bother!' An unsteady, ironic little laugh escaped her. 'It's not that I can't unlock your heart. Not one woman in a million could fit a key to what's not there.'

'Frances, Frances, that sort of remark could bring fireworks! You're so extravagant—your loves and hates, your praise and your condemnations. Anyone with a grain of judgment could see you don't know what you're talking about, but you've any amount of courage. I admire that, if nothing else.'

His voice, though reasonable, had a disquieting sound to it. A dangerous situation could develop because of it. This shadowy flowering wilderness could be a jungle dense with trees and shrubs and thick with leaves underfoot. If Scot made one move Frances would take off like a blue streak of lightning. The small triangle of her face had paled.

He studied it in an enigmatic silence. Bent back against the picturesque bark of a ribbon gum she looked like a small, beautifully shaped bud. He felt unusually exasperated with her, but despite himself, his expression softened. 'Come along, little one, let's call a truce. You're too small to attack, in any case. Just another adorable kid who says what she likes.'

He turned away from her with his swinging vitality, leaving her swaying. 'I'm sorry! I'm sorry!' she called after him, surprising herself. She hadn't meant to say that at all. Scot stopped, alert and motionless, staring at her, and she ran after him. 'I didn't mean to offend you. You make me feel very strongly, but why I can't tell! I'm not usually so outspoken. You just bring out the...'

'...perverse in you!' he supplied. 'All the same, it makes a nice change from the norm. One gets so few opportunities to get told off. I'm taking no chance of losing you until the very minute before you go home.'

'To New Zealand?' she enquired.

He made no reply but took a firm hold of her hand, drawing her along hard so that she was almost skipping over the ground. In this mood he was the benevolent dictator, and she gave a seductive little laugh. 'Consider, David, we might finish up good for one another! I'm willing to be convinced you're a grand person at heart!'

'And you're just a catty little bitch, but very young and desirable. Feel like a cup of coffee?'

'You sound like Chris.'

'I don't feel like Chris—unless he turns you over his knee!'

'Oh no, he's the nicest man in the world!'

'Didn't I say something about a truce? I can behave if you can.'

When he was nice he was terribly nice and all the more need for caution. Frances allowed herself a single glance at him. He seemed to be smiling, a faint quirk to his beautifully cut mouth. He certainly knew how to make love, and the implications of that were enormous and uncomfortable. One could only deduce that he had had any amount of practice. Practice makes perfect, but Scot had an innate skill. Finesse, that was it. Dreadful, when he was only amused and piqued by her.

He looked down at her quickly, cutting off her fine appraisal. 'And what's the conclusion?'

'You could be very cruel!'

'Only with a baby like you. Do tell me what you think of the kitchen. It's Mrs Walker's province normally, but she has the whole day off after last night.'

'She couldn't have done it all on her own,' Frances remarked, remembering the sumptuous supper.

'Just about. Come in, Miss Donovan.' He opened the rear entrance door to let her go ahead.

'Oh, I say! Mother would love this. How fabulous! She's a marvellous cook too.'

'More important, perhaps, are you?'

'Well, actually no. I never get the opportunity. That's the trouble with real artists. They never let anyone else have a go.'

'Perhaps I'm trusting you overmuch letting you make the coffee.'

'I don't think so. Oh, let me have a look at all this. I thought our own place was pretty super, but this! Space and planning and every time-saving appliance. We've got that, but our kitchen is white, very crisp and efficient. This is a kitchen in the round with all those wonderful vistas of the countryside and the central court. What are all these cabinets?'

'Walnut, can't you tell? Rubbed with black wax. Mrs Walker is happy in it, which is the main thing. I'd hate to do the cooking myself.'

'You disappoint me. I'd just about arrived at the conclusion that you could do everything!'

'I didn't say I couldn't do it should the occasion arise, it's just that I wouldn't want to. Don't be overawed by it, the percolator is electric and there's the coffee over there. One heaped dessertspoon to a cup.'

'Thank you, Mr Sutherland. Let's sit at the bench over there. It looks a charming spot. There's obviously more to this kitchen than meets the eye. It's downright romantic!'

'For years to come, one might hope!' He slid into the orange leather-upholstered seat and looked across at her charmingly occupied with precise measurements of coffee. 'Tell me about the argument!'

'I don't know if I should.' Frances hesitated.

'You've decided already! In any case, Frances, I know enough of your grandfather. I've had dealings with him myself.'

She broke off in what she was doing to stare across at him. 'It's the saddest thing in the world,' she said slowly, almost to herself, 'but Grandfather has never learnt to love his own grandson.'

'Does one need to learn?' he asked, equally serious. 'I would have thought it came naturally, like all the best things in life.'

'Not with Grandfather. Perhaps he had such a harsh upbringing himself that he never learnt how —to express himself, I mean.'

'He loves you,' he said without inflection.

'Apparently.'

'Then again we might consider that it's easier for a man to outwardly demonstrate his love for a daughter or a granddaughter. A certain amount of indulgence is taken for granted. One takes a tougher line with the male of the species—all excepting mothers, of course!'

'No, it's not that!' she said thoughtfully, plugging in the appliance. 'Grandfather doesn't love Dario, and Dario knows. He has such a generous, philosophic nature it hasn't hardened him or made him bitter.'

'Merely his mother!' Sutherland supplied. 'Dario might have done better with your red hair.'

'My father had red hair,' she said tragically. 'So did my Uncle Desmond. It didn't make all that much difference. My mother will never speak of her life at Sugar Hill.'

'Yet the fact remains, she found it necessary to cross the Tasman to win her independence.'

'She was the lucky one!'

'Not *lucky* at all, Frances,' he said rather curtly. 'Luck, I would say, had very little to do with it. Your mother made a decision that called for great courage. It couldn't have been easy for her to pull up all her roots—a widow with a young child. At least with your grandfather she was assured of financial security, a lot more important than you seem to think. No, she picked herself up and her small daughter and made a new life for herself. Such courage and initiative deserves to be rewarded. In her case it was. It's as plain as that tip-tilted nose of yours that you've had the benefit of a happy childhood. It gives one a head start that often can't be beaten. Dario had no such thing.'

'Yet you want to take Sugar Hill off him?'

His eyes narrowed over her flushed face. 'What an absurd charge! Dario doesn't *want* Sugar Hill, I thought you knew that. One would have to be a fool to turn him to farming. He's a born artist. What he needs now is hard work and expanding his horizons. We have more than enough farmers. Sugar is a thriving industry. We'll never have enough artists. I believe he could make a big name for himself.'

'Yet he won't make a move by himself He allows Grandfather to browbeat him in so many ways. Then again, in other ways that matter, he's rather lazy. I can see both sides. Rosa, I think, hates my grandfather.' She tightened her hand that was trembling slightly, feeling his eyes on her—very penetrating eyes, a brain that knew exactly what she was thinking. 'Why am I telling you all this?' she accused him. 'It sounds disloyal.'

'Oh, nonsense! You trust me in one way if not in another. Isn't that ready yet, the red light is on.'

'Who's making this coffee?' she asked him as if she'd done it one hundred times. 'Coffee cups, where?'

'Use those on that little stand affair,' he said, obviously not interested in a further search. 'Has your grandfather spoken to you about his plans for you and Dario?'

'What plans?'

'Don't play dumb, Francesca, leave that to the blondes.'

'Patrice?' she queried waspishly, and brought the stylish little coffee cups over to him, then went back for the coffee. 'Cream, sugar?'

'Two sugar, that's the lot. Stop fidgeting, little one. Sit down, for God's sake. Sugar here. Raw, I like it.'

'Me too!' Frances said ungrammatically, doggedly stirring her coffee. She had discovered it was a mistake to sit down beside him almost touching his shoulder. There was a very clean, male scent about him, a physical aura it was impossible to ignore. An outrageously attractive man. He must have been told so before, a million times, probably all round the world. Women could make themselves clear in any language. South American women in particular were luscious. 'I could be of the greatest help to Dario,' she announced, not entirely in control of herself. 'He needs someone to drive him along.'

'Let someone else do it!' Scot suggested at once. 'My advice, and first class. I've seen enough misalliances. Madellana Rossi would suit him very well. Don't interfere there.'

'I wouldn't have thought so from the little I've seen of her,' she said into her steaming cup.

'You don't know, Francesca. You don't know

Madellana either. She adores Dario—she always has, from childhood I understand. She makes no bones about it. Neither does her family.'

'That's not a good enough reason.'

'Don't you believe it!' he scoffed at her gently, but his silvery eyes were as sharp as a sword. 'Dario and Madellana share a common heritage. Dario is part Italian—the upper part, you must remember this. Italians have very strong family ties. The family is everything, particularly Mamma. What she says goes! You surely don't think Rosa won't always be around? She will, and Dario will want it that way. In fact, I'll go a step further. Rosa will always have the final say with her son and Dario will uphold her judgment. Madellana at least will know what to expect. She's been brought up that way herself. There are so many things to argue about in marriage one might hope to have a few things straight. Just imagine you and Rosa thrown together, sharing the same house! You with red hair!'

'Dario would always be fair to his wife,' she said tonelessly.

'Don't preach to the converted, girl! Dario is a born diplomat—he would always avoid unpleasantness. On the other hand, a little fire-eater like you would always meet it head on. Dario would fall on his feet while you would wear yourself out from sheer nervous exhaustion—which brings me to the all-important question: Just how far have you gone with this thing in your own mind? Put down that cup and answer me.'

Her hair swung forward in a massy curtain, brilliant in a chink of sunlight, her face hidden. 'I'm going to wait until I see the painting,' she said, all out to be obstructive. 'That should determine a lot of things.'

Scot brought his own cup down rather hard. 'How you never shirk talking nonsense! Come and see the horses, they've got more sense than you.'

'As long as they're not better looking,' she said impertinently.

'They're not!' He stood quite still, staring down at her intently. 'And they're classy enough at that.'

'Yet you don't approve of me?'

'I don't, but buck up! I never scrap any charitable scheme once I've started out on it.'

'And I'm charity?' she said, rather foolishly hurt.

'The sweetest little bit of charity in the world, sister woman! Are you going to get up?'

'Of course!' Swiftly she slid out from behind the circular bench. He was obviously on the point of hurling her over, and it struck her again what an impatient man he was. Both of them spun their heads around, arrested by the sound of an unmistakable female voice that floated into the inner court, quickly followed up by the clatter of platform soles.

'Yoo-hoo, darling! Yoo-hoo, Scot!'

'Do all your visitors walk in unannounced?' Frances burst out maliciously.

'She did say yoo-hoo—inelegant, but it serves,' he replied blandly.

'I'll be on my way.'

'Oh, calm down, little idiot!' he said, briskly ignoring her determination to be somewhere else. 'It was you I invited!'

'Well, I'd rather not stay on, if it's all the same with you.'

'Well, it isn't!'

'I can see the horses another day, surely?'

'If you don't stay, there won't *be* another day,' he

said flatly.

'Charming! I would have thought you'd be elated by the sexy Patrice's unexpected visit.'

'So you think she's sexy, do you?' he broke off to say, apparently genuinely interested in her answer.

'Well, isn't she? What a damned fool question to ask me!'

But Patrice had caught sight of her quarry, super-sophisticated in a white linen safari pants suit with a black and white polka-dot silk shirt and a few interesting trinkets slung about all this.

'Scot!'

Instantly he moved out towards her, all the life and welcome in his voice imaginable. 'Patrice! What an unexpected pleasure!'

Patrice, a tall girl, brushed her mouth against his cheek with all the enthusiasm she was capable of. 'Sorry to barge in on you like this, Scot, but Daddy has a dear friend he'd like you to meet—Gerald Henderson. He only arrived about two hours ago from the Reef. He didn't want to miss it before he went on home to England. He's terribly interested in your horses and of course, Daddy knew you'd love us to bring him along.'

'Yes, of course!' Scot responded, and Frances judged it time to make her entrance and departure in one flash. She walked out into the sunlight, amused in spite of herself by the look of ludicrous amazement on Patrice's face—a kind of parlour-maid caught dallying with the master of the house with the would-be mistress arrived on the scene.

'Oh, it's you?' Patrice managed, rather badly at variance with her sophisticated appearance.

'How are you, Miss Langford?' said Frances. 'I was just on the point of leaving as you arrived. Do you mind, David?'

'You're not going yet, *Fran*,' Scot Sutherland said with feigned lightness, his eyes on his youngest guest brilliantly steely, as though willing her to make a scene.

'Oh, there you are!'

A party of three joined the group—a pleasantly prosperous, deeply tanned man in his early sixties, the man who had spoken, a tremendously well groomed woman who could only be Patrice's mother and the holidaying Englishman, judging by the fine case of sunburn on his clear, pale skin. The men were smiling, Mrs Langford undetermined on the proper course, but instantly aware of the undercurrents. Introductions began all over again, the men shaking hands with uncontrived bonhomie, the women, the Langford women, silently proclaiming their territorial rights.

'Delighted to meet you,' Frances said to Mrs Langford, entranced by the wary expression on the older woman's long, haughty face, a replica of her daughter's without the sex appeal. Had she ever had it? Frances couldn't tell, but she had the notion that Patrice had already filled in her mother with all the relevant details of the party the night before. Mrs Langford's expression was not: who is this girl, but rather, what is she doing here?

''Tell me, what brings you to our shores, my dear?' Mrs Langford said mock-pleasantly as they all predictably fell into two different camps—men, women. 'A holiday? Pleasure trip?'

Feigning she didn't already know, Frances thought. 'Actually, I've come home to live with my grandfather, Mrs Langford,' she said on a firm note, set on complicating matters further.

Something was allowed to click over in Mrs Langford's head. She chanced a malignant look at

Frances, protected by the broad shoulders of the Englishman. 'Oh, *Donovan!*' she said, brightly re-thinking. 'Of course. Vincent Donovan's grand-daughter. How could I have forgotten? Patrice was saying something about it, but I didn't quite com-prehend, I suppose. But surely you'll be anxious to return to your people, my dear? One gets so lonely!'

'My people live at Sugar Hill as well, Mrs Lang-ford,' Frances retorted with a faint down-to-earth smile that said plainly: who do you think you're kidding? All women knew the code.

Mrs Langford understood well enough, and gave a huffy smile in return. She turned her silver mink head none too calmly towards her daughter. 'You'll have to arrange a few outings for Frances before she goes back.'

'No hurry at all, Patrice,' Frances supplied, wav-ing her hand as if she had all the time in the world. 'I could very well be here for the best part of a year!'

'But what is your work?' Mrs Langford asked with unusual vehemence. 'No young girl should be without ambition.'

'I've plenty of that!' Frances smiled, allowing her eyes to rest on Scot Sutherland's animated dark profile. 'As a matter of fact, I hope to make my mark here in North Queensland.'

'Is that so?' Sharply Mrs Langford chopped her off, to give her daughter a very flat-eyed glance. The position was more serious than she had been led to believe.

'David's place is an absolute bijou!' Frances went on, resting her pointed chin in her hands.

'Naturally!' Vera Langford said. No need for any outsider to tell her that. 'As I expect you know,

Scot and Patrice have been very close friends for a year or more past. We've been in on all Scot's plans right from the beginning. We've seen the house and stud grow. We dearly love Scot and he us, I feel. Of course he has far more in common with Patrice than anyone else.'

'I had heard some such thing!' Frances said, smiling radiantly at the frigid Patrice. 'Lucky thing, you. He's been particularly pleasant to me, too!' she added, playing the part of the simple country bumpkin to the hilt. 'The party last night and then to come over to Sugar Hill for me this afternoon . . . I was thrilled! We've just had coffee. It's still hot, would you like some?'

'Thank you, no!' said Patrice, speaking for the first time, very hard and fast. 'We had a hearty luncheon!'

What on, nails? Frances thought, judging by the set of Patrice's mouth. The mother too was looking vaguely unstrung, staring at this small redheaded intruder in their midst in her expensive slacks and revoltingly pretty shirt that made so much of her colouring. For once Patrice didn't appear to be coming off best, and Vera Langford was understandably upset. She continued to stare at Frances as if she was one of the damnedest people she had ever met. Evidently there was something very strange in her presence at the Sutherland place, Frances concluded. Irritated and on her mettle, she chatted on to the two women, ignoring their mono-syllabic answers and treating them as the honoured visiting team and she on her home ground. It gave her enormous private satisfaction. It would do them both the world of good to think Patrice had a serious known competitor for once. She too could aspire to darling Scot and his fabulous country mansion. What a fool she was not to have thought of this last night. It would have brightened up the evening no end. She must be convincing, for both women were looking at her with marked attention and almost but not quite snarling. Whatever their exact expression it said quite clearly it was absolutely vital to get Frances back to New Zealand as soon as possible or bring in reinforcements. Both women were dedicated and resourceful and not over-scrupulous at bringing their combined power to bear on the situation. Patrice's welfare was being threatened. After all, there weren't that many men suitable in the far North. Scot Sutherland was ideal. Anywhere. Together, at home, they would work out the details of a counter-campaign. The girl, if a prattling ingénue, was strikingly pretty and men, even the best of them, were fools about such things.

Much later, circling the property in the Land-Rover, Frances had tired of her role. She had plenty of spirit and a marked sense of the ridiculous, but as Scot Sutherland had so rightly observed, not all that much stamina. It was Patrice and her mother who had that. Two against one and a survival of the fittest. Frances had read about such women, but she had never truly believed in them. Now they were here in front of her eyes, determined not to give an inch. Scot Sutherland was theirs. They were the pioneers and no little New Zealand invader was going to reap *their* reward.

But the horses were gorgeous, with their unique way of exciting the imagination. Gerald Henderson, an experienced horseman with a first-class critical eye, was obviously finding the whole afternoon a joy. Charles Langford too, very much at home in lush paddocks 'full of beauties', as he put it. Not so his womenfolk. Competent horsewomen both of them, they had more important business on hand: to get straight the issue of Scot Sutherland. Every look, every word, every gesture was directed solely towards making the position clear to a blind man.

Frances, for her part, got the message loud and clear, but by this time she was tired of the whole thing. Now when she was sick of nonsense, they wanted to start. It was too bad. She wanted to be with the men and share their uncomplicated admiration. The love of horses was inbred in her too, yet close enough to see the network of veins under the thin, gleaming skin, she discovered in herself a curious nervousness, a marked respect for their height and effortless power, those slender, thrusting legs. Her father had been killed by such a flying hoof—she could never forget that. At the same time, she could scarcely condemn horses for what had been on her father's part, a calculated risk that had tragically failed. Her father had known the horse was a rogue, a 'bad 'un' before he had ever tried to edge into the saddle. What a precarious hold one had on life even at the best of times. Surely her father should have thought of his wife and child? But men were often careless about danger.

Sutherland, catching sight of her intense little face, somehow managed to isolate her from the other women, which wasn't all that easy considering the way Patrice and her mother had been trying to hem him in. 'All right, young Donovan?' he asked, giving her a brief, mocking smile that had the effect of making her square her shoulders again.

'Yes, of course. I'm loving it! A little nervous too, for some reason,' she admitted.

'Incredibly so!' he murmured with a deep, humorous inflection. 'You have the same pent-up, fiery look about you as my thoroughbreds. Ready to fly off the handle at a moment's notice.'

'As bad as that?' she asked wryly.

He nodded his dark head and didn't bother answering, studying her with a look of understanding and indulgence as if she was a very familiar species. In fact in almost exactly the same way as his precious horses, she looked rather frail for all her spirit and vulnerable because of it.

'My father was killed in a riding accident,' she found herself explaining.

'Yes, I know.'

'Oh, how?'

'I imagine everyone who lives in this part of the world knows that, Frances,' he said in an easy reassuring tone. 'The Langfords would know, so take that high-strung expression off your face. You look ready to run until you drop in your tracks if either of them comes near you again. Now, just stay by my side for a while and listen. Gerald can hold the fort for a while. Nice chap that, and he knows what he's talking about. The horse they're all admiring at the moment is Black Domino, my resident glamour stallion. Spectacular, isn't he? It's common knowledge since the Press got hold of it, so I'll tell you I paid close on a half a million dollars for him last August, before the start of the mating season. He's an import from the blue grass country of Kentucky. Why he's so valuable is he has an almost legendary reputation as a foal getter able to bequeath his own star quality with fantastic reliability. His stud fee, consequently, is astronomical to anyone outside the business. He'll serve the best mares in the country. Ladies of the blood, nothing less. As you can see, he's marked as a thoroughbred by his extreme height. He's seventeen hands with a very long horizontal stretch, slender in the rear girth but plenty of depth through the heart. I suppose you could say a thoroughbred *is* heart, bred to run and run and outstrip all his fellows. Nothing can touch him but the quarter horse and then over a short distance. The quarter mile, hence the name. We're coming to my quarter horses shortly, so you'll be able to appreciate the differences in confrontation. Bored?'

'Good heavens, no,' she said, startled that he should even ask.

Black Domino suddenly shied away across the grass, propelling his long slender legs upwards towards the slopes. He looked a magical sight, the determination and thrust, mane and tail flowing backwards in the breeze. 'He's very splendid, isn't he?' Frances said, smiling. Not a question but a simple statement of fact. He was splendid and absolutely splendidly free. 'What a marvellous way to cover the ground.'

'Up to twenty-four feet in one sequence.'

'Is that good?'

'The great Man o' War only did twenty-five.' He was smiling faintly at her ignorance, in a different, relaxed mood, his lean cheeks creased, his dark head inclined rather protectively towards her. For no other reason her heart suddenly melted. She was completely unable to look away fom him, intensely aware of him, so that it seemed the sight and sound of him was acting on her like a powerful, intoxicating stimulant. It was an odd moment full of an unutterable bitter-sweet pleasure and she wished she could hold on to the moment for ever. His silvery eyes were moving slowly over her face, coming to rest where the pulse of life beat in her creamy young throat, but if he felt even a tiny, flicking flame of what she was experiencing, he gave no sign, his voice lazy and confident and faintly bantering. 'Ready to move on?'

'Yes!' she said, the moment slipping through her fingers. Her face flushed and she averted it quickly, swinging her bright head towards the opposite paddock with its immaculate white rails.

'You play polo, don't you? Dario was saying you're a wonderful player!'

'That's very generous of him,' he smiled. 'I'm addicted to the game at any rate. Dario has played on my team many a time. He's a good hard-hitting player himself, but being Dario his game depends a lot on his mood—the artistic temperament, I suppose. It usually invests the scene with a whole lot of colour. Thoroughbreds make brilliant mounts and I do a good business there as well. Most of us around here were riding before we could walk—a slight exaggeration, but close enough. You don't ride yourself?'

Frances clasped her delicate hands quietly and moved over to lean against the white rails, feeling the firm springy turf under her feet: 'I've never had the opportunity, yet horses seem as familiar to me as anything I've ever known. These sights, these sounds, manes and tails whipping in the breeze, those tall pine trees, the beautiful, never-ending miles of emerald green cane, the red ochre fields lying fallow, the distant purple of the ranges. I was only five years old when I felt all this, yet it's stayed with me with great vividness, more familiar to me than my own beautiful New Zealand. Explain it if you can!'

'Love of the Homeland, child. It doesn't need an

explanation. We've all felt it at different times.' A faint smile curved the edges of his mouth. 'Many a desolate moment I've had at the oddest damned parts of the globe, the mad impulse to throw up the lot and just come on home. Our background, our nationality is part of everything we do and say. It leaves a stamp on us wherever our wanderings. My grandparents on both sides came from Scotland, yet I've never been taken for anything else but an Australian and it's not because of my accent, because I've been told repeatedly I have none.'

'No, that's true. It's a sort of cosmopolitan voice, perhaps it's your tan?' she smiled. 'Outside of a Navajo Indian I don't think anyone else goes that exact colour. Even Dario retains that dark golden olive. Dario, of course, looks almost pure Italian. It's fascinating really, ancestry. Are you going to teach me to ride?'

'If you're an especially good girl.'

'I'll just have to be, won't I? I've a feeling we won't be seeing much of Dario now that he's started out on his creative burst.'

'Good for him!' Scot Sutherland said with surprising seriousness. 'There's only one small hitch, young Francés, it's harvesting time. The crops are at their peak of maturity. He'll have to make a real effort to get it all to the mill. Your grandfather can't give all the orders like he used to, and on one could expect him to at his age. It might be best if Dario delays his artistic career until after that cane is all in. The harvesters will do most of the work, but the mill requires a high degree of cleanliness from the crop. I gather Dario slipped up there the last time—too much extraneous matter and some untopped stalks. It will affect the value of the delivery. Your grandfather might not need the money, but Dario, for his own sake, needs to get the job done well.'

'Perhaps you could talk to him about it?' she suggested, a little worried expression on her face.

'I could, young Donovan, but I'm not exactly in your grandfather's good books. He would consider it none of my business, which I'm bound to say, it isn't, except for that tiny line between your brows.'

'What's to happen to Sugar Hill?' she asked him. 'It's something Grandfather couldn't bear to lose.'

'He will lose it when he loses his hold on life, Frances,' he said soberly. 'A poignant fact. In the end, Dario will go his own way. Another life is reaching out for him, not under this timeless sky. Your grandfather has been a very strong man, but he seems to have destroyed many who have come in contact with him. Now his life is almost spent, Dario has a chance—otherwise, who knows, history might repeat itself. I offered your grandfather a great deal of money once for Desmond Donovan's portfolios—your Uncle Desmond, that is. He had a great talent. He made hundreds and hundreds of sketches of horses and I'd give anything to have them. So would a lot of people, believe it or not.'

'But surely Grandfather ...' she protested loyally, but he cut her off.

'... your grandfather is not holding on to the sketches because he treasures his son's work. He's not so far as I know bequeathing them to his grandson, a natural legacy. He simply doesn't think much of that and can't for the life of him see why anyone else should. The miracle is, he hasn't burnt them.'

'God forbid!' Frances said piously. She had pored for hours over those sketches which were in their way superb. 'The really ironic part is all our talent, and I have a slight talent myself, came from Grandfather. That's why he takes no notice of anyone else. He told me himself he could draw a damned sight better than Uncle Desmond, and Grandfather, to be fair, makes no false claims. He was bred to the land and nothing else matters. Drawing horses is only a boy's hobby, don't you see?'

'What if I do?' he said, touching a finger to the tiny pleat between her winging dark brows. 'Get your grandfather to leave *you* the sketches, Frances.'

'I won't give them to you,' she said breathlessly, drawing away.

'That goes without saying, Frances Donovan, a chip off the old block.'

'I'll smuggle them out and show them to you,' she promised, perversely now, trying to please him. 'Oh, don't stride away from me like that, David,' she begged him. 'Patrice and her mother are desperate to seize their moment.'

'Then come along,' he said a shade impatiently, holding out his hand.

'Horses have such an aura of romance, haven't they?' she said, searching his dark face for any further sign of displeasure.

'And why not? They have a legendary history. Fellow soldiers of the ancient world carrying the warrior into battle, leading the chariot charge. The Hittites, Assyria, Babylonia, Egypt and Persia, mighty Greece and Rome rose and fell with their cavalry. Alexander was said to have been a brilliant equestrian, and I'm sure he was. Then think of the knights of the Middle Ages with all their splendid gear and blazing heraldry, the American Civil War with both sides depending on their cavalry, our own tragic Charge of the Light Brigade at Balaclava that nearly brought the military career of the horse to a close. That came with the Second World War and proud mounted Poland being-massacred by the German tanks. The horse has won the right to relax and do what he does best, give endless hours of pleasure and relaxation, entertainment to millions.

'He still works, of course,' Scot went on, 'and nowhere more than in our Outback, but even there he's treated more as a friend and companion, sometimes a man's only companion for long lonely weeks on end. And this beautiful little creature coming towards us is Princess Shazima, a pure bred Arabian mare. As you can see, she has the absolute, loving freedom of the stud, and so she should with her dazzling ancestry. A princess of the desert looking pretty much as her ancestors must have looked clean back to Mohammed.'

As he was speaking, the little mare, who had formed a very special attachment for her human master, put her peculiarly sculptured head over the rail and began to nudge Scot in the sweetest way possible. Frances put out her own hand and caressed the velvety muzzle.

'What enormous doe eyes set further down the face, aren't they?'

'You're very observant. It must be your training. The eyes, the prominent forehead and the dish into the nose are characteristics of the Arab. Shazima, though she's always sweet-tempered and exceptionally intelligent, considers herself a cut above the working horses, the quarter horses, and they're a good-looking breed, but much more rugged than the thoroughbred or my little pure-bred Arab here. We'll have to join the others when I show you them. Henderson is particularly interested in them and the ladies are getting restive. I think they would like your company again.'

'Just to tell me yet again that "darling Scot" is their property.'

'I'm no woman's property, little one. I thought I told you that.'

'Don't tell *me*, tell Patrice,' she said impudently.

'Yes, Patrice is certainly interested,' he said smoothly. 'She's a highly competent horsewoman as well.'

'I understand, sir,' she murmured with that little audacious flicker of temper that so alarmed her mother. 'The messages I've received this afternoon! All very clear and all understood. Let's please rejoin the group!'

'Frances, Frances!' he said, his narrowed eyes mocking her, 'what would you do if I really did wash my hands of you?'

'Walk home,' she said succinctly.

'I've a feeling you'll be doing that presently.'

'All right, I surrender. God knows I don't want to.'

'But you will! The only smart thing you've done this afternoon. To continue the way you're going would be to fight a hopeless war. I'm much tougher than you are, young Donovan.'

'That's possible! I notice you're not this way with Patrice.'

'What way?'

'Very high-hat, arrogant!'

'I knew what was coming, but I didn't think you'd be so foolish,' he said, a deceptively charming smile on his face for the benefit of the others, but his hand bit hard into the crook of her arm.

'I shall scream!' she said equally soft, knowing full well she wouldn't.

'You can't afford to, Frances. You don't know me well enough. You're not, for instance, entirely sure what I would do.'

'You're quite right! Handling women is child's play to you.'

'I know how to handle *you* well enough! Kissing you makes it a lot harder for you to talk.'

'I wish you wouldn't speak about that,' she said swiftly, her cheeks flaming. 'That was a mistake.'

'I agree.'

'I say, you two aren't fighting, are you?' Patrice enquired with something like delight. It was perfectly plain from the flags of colour in the Donovan girl's cheeks, the silvery ice-cold chips in Scot's strange, light eyes. How perfectly marvellous! she thought on a little wave of feline triumph. It was quite possible, as Mother said, the girl might be her own worst enemy. She was far too articulate and men really didn't like women who talked too much. Patrice tended towards long silences herself and she rather thought Scot appreciated them of late. Busy men didn't want to be bothered with a lot of backchat.

Almost sick with jealous anxiety for most of the afternoon, it was a wonderful thing to sense the aura of sexual antagonism that hung around those two like a thick veil of smoke. Her self-confidence came back in a rush and Mother, loyal creature that she was, wasted no time in getting to the Donovan girl's side, thoughtless of her own pleasure, allowing her daughter her opportunity to shine. It had become a habit and Vera Langford was desperately pinning her own and her daughter's hopes on this one man, Scot Sutherland, handsome and wealthy with a life style Patrice craved. This mysterious Donovan girl had to go, but now, wonder of wonders, it appeared she had worked that out herself. It was the easiest thing on earth to get what you wanted if you knew how.

Patrice, her voice stronger, slightly affected and penetrating, moved over to where Sutherland's whipcord body was arched over the rail, saying something to Gerald Henderson that made the Englishman burst into hearty laughter. 'This afternoon has been the most....' words failed her and she flung her hand over Sutherland's own.... *marvellous* experience. Gerald, you're loving it, aren't you?'

Gerald said yes, giving Frances a rather playful smile, then suddenly as though he had come to a decision, gracefully took the younger girl's arm, questioning her in a very friendly fashion about New Zealand, the South Island in particular, where he had several relatives.

Relieved beyond measure to have been rescued from Mrs Langford, Frances went quietly, moving in her light gliding fashion beside the stockily built Englishman. In no time at all they had started up a pleasant, unforced conversation, leaving Patrice with Scot Sutherland, her beautifully made up face radiant and secure. She could scarcely believe now she had even worried about the girl. Scot had an engaging cynical smile on his shapely mouth that said eloquently enough: what was another pretty girl? He turned back to smile at Patrice and she was swallowed up in a yawning abyss of physical and material desire. To land a matrimonial prize like Scot Sutherland would make up for all the long torture of having her four front teeth capped.

CHAPTER SEVEN

IT was the hardest thing in the world to make a still model appear to be in motion, yet somehow he had managed it. The size and structure of the slender, graceful body, the lovely limbs, the arms and legs, the play of muscle and the satiny young skin that covered it. It was very accurate as a construction, very fluid and confident. There was no doubt it was Frances, though it was essentially an action portrait with most of the emphasis placed on movement rather than faithfully reproducing his cousin's lovely, piquant face. It had cost him almost a twenty-four-hour day, long hours in the fields with the pre-harvest and burn-off and nights without sleep, but Dario was particularly proud of it.

Frances had been of enormous help, though she wasn't in one sense the best model in the world, being far too volatile to hold poses for long. He had made certain of it all by eye and pencil measurements and the stunningly clear photographic image of his model forever in his mind. Every day the exact position of her arms in a port de bras or arabesque or whatever, he couldn't remember the ballet terms, had varied slightly, the bend of the raised leg, the position of the head, the left arm bent at the elbow, the hand turned in towards the shoulder, the right arm fully extended, both hands very supple and graceful. What perfect control she had over that beautiful body of hers. The long years of training had imparted a tremendous chic even to the way she turned her head. It was his most ambitious work, the most difficult, but he had conquered it.

Now at last he realised he had a duty to himself as an artist. After this he could call himself that with absolute conviction. There were a young man's tears in his eyes and being nearly all Italian he didn't blink them away fiercely. Sometimes it was good to cry. Better, it was healthy. Were Francesca here, he would cover her in kisses. She had made her costume herself from a sketch he had drawn her. He wanted no classical tutu but more what she finally came up with—a brief, heart-shaped wisp of bodice that followed the curves of the breast and exposed their tender cleft and a knee-length cloud of tulle through which the full length of the right leg *en pointe* showed luminously. The tights and pale pink satin ballet shoes she had borrowed—from where Dario never asked and actually didn't care.

Up in the loft, Dario felt the strong draught of wind as the barn door was flung open. He swung his head about eagerly.

'Fran? Come up. It's almost finished, and if someone doesn't tell me pretty soon I'm a genius I'll fall prey to the great beast of the drink!'

There was a momentary silence and a darkly amused voice called up to him: 'If it's an opinion you want, you'll get it, but a drinking companion will have to wait till tonight.'

'Dave!' Moving with fresh vitality, for he was in reality very tired, Dario picked up an old rag and wiped his stained and battered hands. The spider flowers with their sharp thorns had made a real mess of them and made things difficult for the harvester as well. He hadn't paid enough attention to weed control. As a farmer he was a failure. The weeds in the cane were certain to increase harvesting costs and the Old Man would want to know why. What a pity the harvester couldn't tell the weeds from the cane but harvested them together. Ah well!

By the time he had turned around Scot Sutherland had hoisted himself into the loft, his very attractive smile at the ready. It just as soon faded.

'Good God!' he said in a curiously strained way.

Dario coloured violently, jerking his head about, following the direction of those light, glacial eyes. The dark circles under his own eyes were never more apparent than when the flush faded. Had he failed? Was it all in his own mind, the wonderful feeling of elation, the knowledge that he had finally made the grade? Dave was no fool. His judgment was excellent. He had a fine modern collection and he had walked the great galleries of the world. Now he was moving in his lithe, purposeful way, going straight towards the painting, his eyes riveted on the light almost flying body, released for the dance as though if she couldn't dance she would die.

'Say something!' Dario crackled, powerfully nervous.

'Better still, applaud,' Scot said almost under his breath, but Dario broke out into the sweat of relief. It dewed his fine, rounded brow and ran into his thick black eyelashes.

Scot said nothing more but continued to examine the portrait as if he had all the time in the world and nothing better he would wish to do. 'One can almost hear the music. Did you play any, by the way?'

'That was Francesca's idea,' Dario said with a great rush of happiness. 'There must be the music, she said. It was pretty terrible, as it happened, on Grandfather's old gramophone, but it was enough for her.'

'Obviously,' Scot said, rather dryly. 'She looks quite magical. The first time I ever saw her, flying for me, I noticed she had a very beautiful way of moving. Forget the extraordinary temper. Now it seems we have Frances' poetic quality, your brilliance and a very exciting painting. I congratulate you, *amico*, I've always told you you have an unusual gift. This is magnificent.'

'And you wouldn't say so if you didn't think so,' Dario said happily, reassured beyond measure. 'Glory Hallelujah! If you hadn't said some such thing, Dave, I don't think I would have picked up a brush for the rest of my life!'

Scot shot him a rapier glance. 'To continue now at Sugar Hill would be the real madness. Your grandfather should be very proud of you.'

'Of me? You're looney, Dave.'

'Not at any rate in the way you mean, though I'll admit I'm not quite myself of late. This is quite exceptional. In fact, I want it.'

'Make me a trifling offer,' said Dario, not quite believing in his good fortune. If the painting was to hang in the Sutherland place many influential people would spot it. Society women in particular seemed to hanker after self-portraits.

Scot was eyeing him rather oddly. 'You'd sell?' he said.

'Of course. If you buy it, I'm made. This will excite a great deal more interest than a landscape or a still life.'

'It will at that,' Scot observed, still in that odd, taut voice.

'After all, I shall paint Francesca a million times.'

'How so?'

'I shall marry her, of course,' Dario said, somewhat perplexed by his friend's quick change of mood. Moments like these one realised how very formidable he could be.

'What a damn fool thing!' said Scot, turning back to the portrait. 'Frances is your first cousin.'

'But after all, Dave, we've been introduced. She's not my *aunt*!' said Dario, trying to get the frown off Scot's face.

'*Please!*' Scot said rather testily. 'Paint Frances if you must, but there's no need to marry her.'

'You wouldn't approve?' Dario asked almost ludicrously as if he had taken his friend's approval for granted. More, a huge wedding present, perhaps to be godfather to their first.

'It's none of my business,' Scot said, 'but now you ask, most emphatically, *no*. You need a woman who will wait on you hand and foot, willing slave to make straight your path and leave you all the time in the world to paint. A woman whose existence you will forget for days on end. You've been extremely preoccupied with this, don't forget, and this is only the beginning. Wait until you get into your stride. Frances doesn't fit the bill. In the first place she's not a woman who will be ignored or even who can be ignored, and she needs a whole lot of care herself. She has a very vulnerable look about her—haven't you noticed? You must have, it's here in the painting. Frances is built for speed and flight, not the dedicated régime of being an artist's wife. She'd either pine away or launch into a full-scale affair. She's very emotional.'

'So am I, and I love her!' Dario cried all of a sudden.

'Of course you do. As a cousin,' Scot said repressively. 'I'm sure Frances loves you too in her fashion. I'm very kindly disposed towards you myself on the odd day. One thing is certain, your father would have been proud of you.'

'Yes, Dad would be pleased,' Dario said quietly.

'Pleased isn't the word. In the years to come this whole State of Queensland will claim you as their best friend. I will myself, though I've been pretty rough on you from time to time—now, as it happens. The harvester in the top field has ground to a halt. Young Baker is now taking an ill-deserved snooze. I'd say the weeds are choking the machine. I'd look at it myself if I only had you and Frances to contend with, but I can't go over your grandfather's head.'

'The Old Man's gone into town!' Dario said almost hopefully. 'You know damned well, Dave, I know next to nothing about machinery and the machines seem to know it. *You* can fix anything.'

'Maybe. I have a visitor for you. Waiting very patiently.'

'Oh, who?'

'Madellana. At one time you were nearly inseparable.'

'Oh God, Dave!' Dario groaned. 'Did you have to bring her over? A muster of all the old gang!'

'Keep your voice down!' Scot ordered, suddenly hard. 'She's only outside in the car. That would have struck one hell of a jarring note.'

'It's all right, Scot, I'm here,' a soft, pretty voice said—a voice, moreover, threatened with tears. 'I was so very happy, Dario, at the thought of seeing you, but now I find I am an inconvenience. I'll go!'

Beneath them a small feminine figure sped through the open door, choking with sobs.

'Oh, damn, damn, a million rotten damns!' exclaimed Dario. 'What timing!' His sensitive heart was twisting painfully. Madellana was such a good little thing!

'You'd better get down there and apologise,' Scot suggested. 'Fortunately I have the car keys in my pocket, otherwise you mightn't have time. Anyone would think she was a hideous unwelcome old lady instead of a pretty, healthy girl, an ideal wife and mother.'

'So Mamma says,' Dario said thoughtfully. 'Will you fix the harvester?'

'I might. Where's Frances?'

'The garden, I suppose!' Dario shouted, hastily taking to the stairs. 'She's a real worker, that one, worthy of the name of Donovan. It's so foolish in the hot sun.'

'More like lunatic,' Scot murmured under his breath, turning back to examine the portrait to give Dario the necessary moment to make amends. Madellana's fervent vows to depart were dying off a bit. Certainly, the heartbreaking sobs had stopped. Women! Scot thought cynically, not at all pleasantly disposed towards them this morning. He had a little score to settle with young Donovan. Unlike Madellana, she would have taken to her heels by now, tearing like a small fury away from the place of her humiliation. Madellana, being Madellana, would choose to wait for the car. Frances had turned down a few too many invitations of late, and not very politely at that. The last excuse had been a toothache and he was quite certain she had never suffered one in her life with those small pearly teeth. As it happened he was quite right. Nature and a very vigilant mother had taken care of that.

She was in the garden, trying of all things to copy a certain section of his bush garden, or so it appeared. He must get her a really interesting big boulder, but he had the Old Man to contend with. He paused for a moment studying her bent figure, the sweetly grave, preoccupied expression. She wasn't unlike some tender, uprooted flower herself in that sun-dappled clearing, one golden shaft of light lying across her face and shoulders and lighting her hair to a radiance. It should have moved him, but he felt more like strangling her with her own hair.

He went slowly towards her, for a big man, moving as stealthily as some jungle cat. Frances heard the soft crackle of leaves too late. He was beside her, clipping her waist, hoisting her to her feet, like a puppet on strings, and he a past master at manipulating such inanimate things.

'David!' she said, feeling a crippling loss of confidence. She knew she was at fault in so many ways.

'Yes, *David*,' he said, in his heart-flipping voice. 'No one else calls me David. Dave, Scot, Sutherland —but she calls me David. Think of something quick. Any old excuse will do. What is it today? A boil? A troublesome appendix?'

She looked about them a little wildly. It was one of the very curious things about him, but he frightened her as well. 'I'm not looking for trouble,' she said swiftly.

'There's no door to bolt through, at any rate! Quite early in our acquaintance I noticed you had that tendency.'

'I'm sorry if I've annoyed you,' she said, hating herself for her cowardice. 'I never meant to.'

'Liar!'

'Oh, I am *not*!' Suppressed tears glittered in her wide amber eyes.

'A triple dealer, perhaps. Why, Frances? Why?

Why all the excuses? There must be some motivation. You're not all that unintelligent. In fact, for a woman, you're quite interesting. Yet why is it you're refusing to see me or join in any social gathering at my house? Pretty nearly everyone around here likes to do what is right. It's going to be a long summer and you're making things downright unpleasant.'

'Why should my presence make any difference?' she defended herself.

'It doesn't!' he said curtly. 'The thing is, I'm not used to such frequent rebuffs and in such a manner. Does your grandfather disapprove? You have only to tell me.'

'He hasn't said so.'

'Dario?'

'Of course not!' She shrugged her delicate shoulders. 'Dario considers you his greatest friend and supporter. He won't hear a word against you, which is pretty damned odd when you consider you once tried to throttle him!'

'Naturally I didn't intend to,' he drawled. 'Not him nor anyone else. *Up until now*. I scarcely know you today, Frances, with your tongue not easily found!'

His tall frame registered tension and she drew a small, shuddery breath, darting away from him like a hummingbird, apparently to examine some tiny, wilting plants. 'I suppose I've become accustomed to the more normal run of female,' he hazarded, 'the kind who replies when she's spoken to.'

'What do you expect me to do?' she shouted, showing her own tension, 'start up with joy at your approach?'

'And why not?' he said, dangerously soft. 'It's a whole lot better than doing what you're doing now.'

They studied one another with extreme sensibility, the eternal war of the sexes with the inevitable response.

'It's the physical that wins every time, isn't it?' she said, biting her under lip as if she was in unbearable pain. The knowledge that he made her flesh burn with desire was a terrifying thing.

'What do you mean?' he asked, reaching for her with uninhibited and absolute mastery.

'Force!' she said wildly, her blood singing.

'Force? Why, you little hypocrite, you know what you want as well as I do. Who's forcing you anyway? I'm pretty damned certain I'm not. The one admirable thing about you is your desirability. Nothing else springs to mind!' He put his hand on her face and it was so smooth to the touch it haunted him. What strange power women had! She was no more than a witch drawing him against his will. An answering flash of recognition swept across her face so that she was perfectly still under his caressing hand.

'David?'

Her voice sounded as softly sensual as the night and his own was quite hard. 'Don't try any tricks with me, little witch.'

'Then I'll pass into a world of my own where you don't count.'

'I think I might add indomitable to the desirable,' he said, smiling for the first time. 'You'd never make a willing captive, Frances.'

'Do you want me a captive?'

'Certainly!' he said, with an attractive wry twist of his mouth. 'I've had no meaningful relationship with a woman up to date. Maybe it's my fault—I wouldn't know. I've a natural inclination not to sit

160

about talking twaddle.'

'Are you implying that women are morons?'

'Precisely.'

'Oh no, you do this purposely,' she said, very low, 'trying to hurt!'

'However did I give the plot away?'

'The suggestion is too ridiculous, that's why. The world would have sunk to its doom without a woman's guiding hand. The power behind the throne. The hand that rocks the cradle rules the world, and don't you forget it, David Sutherland. You loved your mother?'

'More, Francesca. I adored her. She was the exception, not the rule. A very witty, intelligent woman.'

'And quite saintly too, and wonderfully tolerant with you for a son.'

'Ask her!' he challenged her. 'She's spending some time with me in the New Year.'

'I'll be home by then,' she said, her heart lunging.

'Really? And here I was led to believe you'd be busy with your trousseau.'

'The thought has crossed my mind, but I've no definite plans. What about you?'

'You're joking! My life is too precious to surrender it to a woman.'

'Of course. Have you seen the painting?'

'I've *bought* it!' he said with no pleasure at all in his voice.

'But I want it for my mother,' she protested, her eyes blazing under her winged eyebrows.

'Mother will have to wait for the next. This is mine. Dario has a big future. There will be another. Not so many of you.'

'He needs a wife to keep him hard at it,' Frances said, in an agitated voice.

'He'll have Mamma and Madellana,' he said smoothly. 'I've brought Madellana over. You might offer her some light refreshment while I try and repair the harvester.'

'What's wrong with it?' she asked, instantly diverted. Grandfather was in such testy moods these days.

'Nothing much, I hope. I'd say the weeds are winding around the moving parts and choking the machine. We'll just have to remove them. On the other hand there could be something seriously wrong with the machine. Dario is the worst farmer in these parts. How he has persisted so long in work that doesn't suit him I'll never know. Your grandfather can well afford to hire any amount of outside help. A lot of these weeds are subject to disease and this can affect the cane. The whole crop could be wiped out.'

'Where are you going now?' she asked him, obviously upset.

'To fix the damned machine. Why should it bother you so much, Frances?'

'Grandfather is only waiting his opportunity with Dario, you know that?'

'His opportunity for what?'

'To cut him out. Out of his life and his will—the lot. I don't want anything. I won't be the bone between them.'

'The only damned sensible thing you've said. How long is your grandfather out? He won't relish my help.'

'Please help us, David! I'll think of anything to cover you.'

'I don't need protection from you, little one. I'll give it. I don't want it. If your grandfather was a much younger man I'd tell him just what I thought. As it is, all of our hands are tied. Age commands respect and an equal amount of restraint. I don't want to upset him more than anyone else.'

'I'll come with you,' she said, drawing a deep breath.

'No, you won't! Stay here. We'll find Madellana. You two should get to know one another. She's a charming girl and quite without vice of any kind. Go easy on her.'

'Why would you say such a thing to me?'

'You have something Madellana can never have, that's why. I know it. Dario knows it and so will Madellana. Be kind to her.'

'I hate you when you talk like that.'

'And I hate you *too!*' he said emphatically, a brilliant flickering light in his eyes. 'Let's both try to bear it.'

A dangerous excitement stirred in his eyes, so that, held by the strange look, she could only return the stare and wait, very small and defenceless. Her skin was electric as if he had touched her.

'Sun-worshipper!' he said, 'why don't you wear a hat?'

'I did once. At school!' Her skin glowed with an even, apricot tan, her amber eyes were shining and red and gold danced along the strands of her hair. She tilted her head a little defiantly, trying to outstare him. He smiled, but there was a flash of something, impatience? in his light eyes.

'Come along, you colourful winged creature as brave as you're foolish, there are things to be done on the instant. With any luck they'll be finished before your grandfather gets back. Dario should be further advanced with the harvesting or he'll be left with standover fields. The mills will stop crushing soon. Maybe some people can do two things at once, but Dario isn't one of them. Whatever he touches in the farming line seems to attract a certain amount of disaster. The farm has been suffering since your Uncle Desmond died. Now things are coming to a head. The Lord only knows why I'm getting involved in all this. It will do me no good. My relations with your grandfather have always been pretty stormy.'

'Perhaps it's because you're so successful,' she said, with some insight. 'Grandfather doesn't really want to die, you know. He wants to go on for ever and ever as powerful and strong as he ever was. He's never had an illness in his life, he's just wearing out. I think he hates the idea of surrendering all this to someone else. Even Dario, his grandson. That's the great pity. It would be easier for him, perhaps, if Dario was more the grandson he wanted.'

'More like *you!*' he said, rather harshly. 'Your grandfather has the curious notion that if you and Dario were to marry, Sugar Hill would come right again. I would say he's brought you here for just that reason.'

'Perhaps,' she admitted.

'You don't really think you hold the solution?' He gave a short laugh, his eyes like forked lightning.

'I could do,' she said, angry now at his implied criticism. Why did he make anger flash and burn in her? *Why?* 'It's very tempting, the idea of becoming the wife of a famous artist. And I'm sure he will be.' It was an all-out effort to taunt him. She couldn't ever remember deliberately trying to anger someone as she was trying to anger David Sutherland. 'Perhaps your mind works in the opposite direction to mine?' she suggested.

He took her arm in a painful grip, almost lifting her off the ground. 'I should be able to let that pass, but I can't! Which just goes to show how I'm slipping. You're right about your mind and wrong about everything else. I can't waste time on any more nonsense. When you meet Madellana take a little notice of her nice, restful ways. There's a lot to be learned from her. Men like girls who curl up in corners.'

'No news!' she crowed, taking her opportunity. 'No news at all. I've long remarked the truth of that. The next time you meet me you'll have to fight to keep from dozing off, I'll be so quiet.'

'That's fine! See it's no idle boast.'

'It isn't! I know your preference for dumb blondes! ... oh dear!' she quailed, 'oh dear, dear!' as he stopped resolutely. 'This is an extremely ticklish moment, but you can't hit me, Saints be praised.'

'Why not?'

The question was delivered so hard and flat it took her a few seconds to recover her self-possession. 'Because I'm a girl, that's why. A good kid.'

'You're lucky, I've noticed. Talking to you is like falling into bed at four o'clock in the morning, exhausted!'

'And I'm very largely taken with you, too!' She broke his grip and danced ahead, throwing him a brilliant, false smile over her shoulder. 'Indeed, Mr Sutherland, I'll go a step further and say I think I'm becoming really fond of you. I'll go find the sweet Madellana, so good and obedient, and chat her up in my outrageous, imbecile fashion.'

'Yes, do,' he said pleasantly. 'I'll hear it all in detail later on.'

'Annoyed?' she asked, not walking on but peering into his handsome, dark face, alerted by the hidden element in his voice. He so embodied everything one had to fight, the autocratic male.

'Don't be a fool,' he smiled, in a narrow-eyed way, very dangerous and alert. 'Of course I'm annoyed. That's what you want, isn't it?'

'Oh yes!' she admitted fervently. 'Sometimes it makes me angry just to look at you.'

'Why?' There was a glint in his eyes and an edge to his voice.

'I don't *know* why!' she said, her voice wavering, her amber eyes very wide in her small golden face. 'Don't look at me like that.'

'Oh, come now, Frances!' he drawled. 'You can't call all the shots. You can't even call half of them.'

She couldn't seem to move, even when his lean, powerful frame was blocking her path. His fingers slid about her wrist, locking, and she shivered like she was cold instead of covered in a prickly heat. 'Are you going to fix the harvester, David,' she cried, frantic to find a safe line of retreat. That might divert him.

'Smile at me and I might,' he said, evidently diverted, for he smiled. 'It would make a nice change.'

'I'll do better than that,' she said, dizzily daring with relief. She lifted herself on tiptoe and pressed home a kiss just under the point of the chin. She was far too jittery to smile at him in his present mood, a butterfly kiss such as a child might give was the smart solution. Just as she was congratulating herself, throwing him an impudent glowing look, she met the brilliant intensity of his eyes. The colour sped into her face and she ducked her bright head.

'Frances, uncertain, coy and hard to please!' he said in a soft, mocking voice, but for her it was like a clap of thunder rolling down from the hills, the reverberations drumming into her. Shocking. Shocking. Shocking her with their intensity. She could hide it from herself no longer. She was in love with him. It was like throwing the master switch and making instant contact. It was sizzling! To love David Sutherland. Shocking, the best word she could find, the most adequate to cover her welter of complex emotions.

She breathed deeply and deeper again. It didn't help. She felt no steadier, the earth-rocking sensation hadn't passed. Panic flitted across her vivid young face, put spots of colour across her wide cheekbones. The only recourse left was to run, put all the distance in the world between them—and stay there!

Hundreds of women had loved David Sutherland. Hundreds—she was sure of it. Right across the world and here he was at thirty-five or thereabouts, an unabashed bachelor, dead set on a good time without complications. Well, he had struck trouble here. She was one of the new breed of women. Modern and financially secure once she got a job. Submission and mock humility was no longer required in a woman, whatever *he* said. A throwback to feudal times and no mistake. His fingers against the network of veins at her wrist were breaking down all her carefully marshalled barriers.

With no apology at all, like some small, outraged, crimson chat, its feathers ruffled, Frances fled the scene....

It was like a nightmare enacted under cascades of light from the big chandelier. The imperious, familiar voice, squeezing the life and the desire to oppose him out of all of them. What a quenchless thirst for power Grandfather had! It was agonising. She was shaken to her heart's core, her emotions reflected on her delicate young face. How to find the words and still appease Grandfather's mind. He had always set his will above anyone else. How he hated objections, and how angrily he would turn on them all. She would relive this scene for hours after they had all gone to bed.

Vincent Donovan was still ranting on, outlining a great destiny for them all. What lordly arrogance, it was never more in evidence. A handsome old man with very fierce amber eyes still burning brightly, he was a tiger and he was ageless. He would never die, not in their minds, and that was an acid fact. Vincent Donovan had bitten deeply into all that had fallen into his power. The whole thing was astonishing, it really was, Frances thought. Grandfather had progressed to hearty good fellowship that sat oddly on him drinking glass after glass of wine without his usual discretion. To say the wrong thing now would be to re-open old raw and bleeding wounds. Grandfather had dominated so many lives. His possessiveness was unlimited, invincible. He had only to suggest a course and others would take it, and why not? He was stronger and more powerful than any of them, indefatigable at getting what he wanted. It was fantastic logic but it worked.

Seated beside her at the dining-room table, Frances could feel the great fury that raged inside Rosa, the hot words that were welling in that strong, sculptured throat. Why had she not said them long ago, Frances thought, instead of waiting until now ready to attack a fierce and perhaps a little crazy old man almost ready to die. Dario across the gleaming red cedar table had a look of idiotic stupefaction on his face. Twenty-five years and his grandfather was still a stranger to him. Grandfather had the makings of a legend. And what plans! ... Frances was to get the money. He would get the farm, the farm he assuredly did not want.

Together, married, as Grandfather so plainly put it, they would share everything, ensuring eternal good fortune for the sacred name of Donovan. It was brilliant, so simple, and so far as Dario was concerned the only good idea his grandfather had ever had. He had not the slightest objection to marrying his beautiful cousin. He could do much, much worse and very little better even in Roma, yet Mamma sat on with the red light of murder in her eyes. Mamma had her heart set on Madellana, that was the trouble and Madellana would have been all right too, had he not met Francesca. Madellana had a little money. All he wanted now was to be left in peace to get on with his real work. Ambition, latent so long, had blazed into life.

Vincent Donovan an unaccustomed flush high on his cheekbones, stared across at his granddaughter, the sparkle of triumph in his still bright eyes. If it was outwitting and outmanoeuvring her it was for her own good. 'You need only catch your breath, my dearest child!' he said. 'Sleep on it. I would die easily knowing you were here at Sugar Hill. Your children with good Donovan blood in them running around the fields.'

It grieved her dreadfully to have to upset him, but it had to be done. To remain silent would be to become another Rosa, a slumbering volcano. 'It's not for me. I can't do it, Grandfather.'

'Why not?' For the first time the old man looked

169

as if he might spin out of control as though a very vital part of his brain was malfunctioning.

'I don't love Dario.'

'You could learn to. You defend him enough.'

'*Cara!*' Dario said across the table, and storm signals flew in Frances's eyes and cheeks.

'Good heavens, Dario, you're not going to trot along meekly with Grandfather's suggestions?'

'Marrying you would be no catastrophe!' said Dario, with unshakable good temper.

'What did Sutherland want?' Vincent Donovan barked as though he had hit on the source of his granddaughter's opposition.

'Just a courtesy call,' said Frances.

'And the Rossi girl? What brought her over as well?'

'I asked her over, actually, Grandfather,' Frances explained. 'She's a very nice girl.'

'With little or nothing to say for herself,' Vincent Donovan snorted. 'I've never had so much as a boo out of her. At least we won't be seeing much of Sutherland, though it's not everyone he honours with his presence. I've had it from Langford that his daughter is to carry off the matrimonial prize of the year!'

'Marry *Dave*?' Dario asked with a startled inflection.

'That's what I said!' the old man said very dryly. 'Incredible!'

'How is that?' The question was very sharp and peremptory, like calling a dog to heel, more Vincent Donovan's style. 'It would seem a suitable match to me, but then you and I have never shared the same viewpoint, Desmond. We'll discuss no more of this tonight. Frances is a spirited girl— she only needs a little period of adjustment to see the wisdom of my plans. Without you, Frances, Desmond will amount to nothing.'

'That's not *true*, Grandfather,' Frances said swiftly, quick-fire anger on her vivid young face. 'Dario is brilliant. He will outstrip us all. Open so many eyes to new horizons, you can't know!'

'I know you care for him more than you think and that settles it!' said Vincent Donovan, not altogether displeased. 'Don't let there be discord between us, my little Fran. Your presence here has given me the happiest weeks of my life. Just think about what I say, quietly and reasonably. I need scarcely add that you will be a very rich woman.'

'I don't give a damn about that!' she said with feverish determination.

'You don't *now*!' her grandfather snapped, rising from the table and throwing his linen napkin down. 'You're young. Wait until age catches up with you a bit. You'll change your mind, I expect. Now kiss me goodnight. I shall read for a while, then I'm going to bed. I've said all that needs to be said. You, Rosa, I notice are silent as usual. God help us all should ever the floodgates open. Set your mind at rest, my dear daughter-in-law, you have been provided for.'

Rosa jerked her head up and her eyes glittered, but she still said nothing. It would be better to be quiet than to explode. In another moment the old man had left the room and they heard his footsteps along the corridor leading to his room.

'You see?' Rosa gave an eerie screech. 'You get the farm. *She* gets the money. Has anyone ever heard such a monstrous plan?'

'It seems quite fair to me, Mamma.'

'*Fair*, you fool!' Rosa burst out in a tremendous monotone, as though they were both, mother and son, condemned to a life of toil and sweat.

'Sugar Hill would fetch a lot of money,' Dario pointed out, not the least concerned by his mother's complaint. 'Dave offered the Old Man a small fortune. The house done up a bit is a wonderful old place, you know. A lot of people like it. Plenty in this town would like to get their hands on the property.'

'Curse him!' said Rosa fiercely. 'He gives nothing to you and treasures to her. She with one little foot in the door!'

'If you don't mind,' Frances said wearily, 'I'll go wash my hair. I can feel an outsize headache coming on. Far from being drunk with joy at my own future enrichment Dario can have the whole damn lot of it. I don't care!'

'And how are you going to refuse it, I should like to know?' Rosa glowered at her.

'I'll work that out if you promise me you won't worry,' Frances retorted with a light, hard humour.

'A-a-h!' Rosa said bitterly with an Italianate gesture of defeat. 'My son is worth a million of you, and he is promised to Madellana.'

'Not that business again, Mamma,' Dario mumbled.

'What kind of a man, are you, Dario?' Frances burst out. 'Are you going to let your mother pick a wife for you?'

'Haven't you learnt yet, he will,' Rosa said with grim humour of her own. 'The world is full of pretty girls, but not so many suitable for my Dario. What's wrong with Madellana? I could hear from your laughter this afternoon that you liked her.'

'Of course I did,' said Frances, jerking her head up, 'but that's not the point. When are you going to grow up, Dario? You sit there like a schoolboy letting your mother arrange your life for you.'

'She is my mother, after all, *cara*,' Dario explained reasonably. 'Had I not met you I would have married Madellana. She's very sweet and amiable and she wouldn't bother me when I'm working.'

'In other words she'll know what to expect. What a marvellous match!'

'But for the money!' Rosa said with deadly accuracy. 'Nothing can take its place.'

'How strange life is!' Dario mused, stroking his dark olive chin. 'To cross the Tasman. To meet your grandfather and cousin. Could we not marry, little one? I swear I would never make you unhappy.'

'You would be making *me* unhappy,' Rosa cried, springing to her feet with great grace for a big woman. 'I'm not set against Francesca blindly. I see and I know what is right. You don't suit! Don't shrug it aside, my son, as if it's of no importance. There's a new land and a new life waiting for us. Madellana will fit in, your cousin won't. There are many reasons for this, and in your heart you must know them.'

'I know Francesca has some magic in her that Madellana lacks,' Dario said rather painfully.

'Marriage would be intolerable without love, Dario,' Frances said, her face softening. 'Love is the centre of life.'

'Madellana loves me,' Dario pointed out in a distant voice.

'Well, that's it, then!' said Frances. 'I'll be turning in. Goodnight.'

'*Cara!*' Dario burst out wretchedly, jumping up from the table, but his mother stopped him with stunning abruptness.

'Sit down, my son. Can't you see your cousin wishes to escape us?'

'What? ... Oh, *yes!*' Dario said with a spurt of agony. 'You and Francesca would never get on. How you and Madellana get on I can never imagine.'

'Don't hit out at your mother who loves you,' Rosa groaned. 'When we leave this place we will forget it for ever.'

'I'll never forget Francesca, and I'll not forget Grandfather either. Neither will you, Mamma. I loathe myself that I've taken so long to find myself. I'm a bit of a coward—I don't often admit it, but it's the truth. Anything for a quiet life, that's me. At the heart of my desire is peace.'

'And you think you would get peace with your cousin?' Rosa shouted. 'I knew from the moment she came into this house you would never get that. What you feel is the fascination of a very unusual face. I can see how remarkably vivid the girl is. Do you think *I* am blind? I have worried myself ill about this. I remember the day you were born, my son. I dedicated my life to you then. I somehow knew you were meant for great things. Even the nurse said you had a wonderful head.'

'They all say that, Mamma!' Dario said hoarsely. 'It's good manners to a new mother. Help them to rejoice and that sort of thing.'

'The very day you were born ...' Rosa continued, ignoring him. 'You are so innocent, my son. We women are the ancient ones and your grandfather is a very sinister old man.'

'For some reason, Mamma, I don't want you to talk about him. I think I'll go into town.'

'Go over and talk to Madellana,' Rosa suggested nervously. 'If nothing else she is a very sensible girl.

Also she loves you so much it is possible she may tell you how to win your cousin. Ironic, is it not? Once you thought a great deal of Madellana. How shameful that you desert her now. But do what you will, my son. Take care of yourself, and don't drive too fast,' Rosa cautioned, standing back, proud and alone. 'What does it matter if you sound the death knell to my dreams? I have longed for grand-children, but not, please, with red hair. To think I have worked myself nearly blind for you! We women have always had to defend ourselves against all the world. I shall go to my room and pray.'

'At any rate keep out of Frances' way,' Dario said, unexpectedly hard. 'I'm little caring tonight whether I live or die!'

He turned and started towards the door, dizzy with his tensions, hearing his mother's beseeching voice in his ear: 'Wear a tie!'

How absurd life was, he thought. Women brought farce into every situation. How like Mamma to think he would still go on to the Rossis'. How like him to almost want to go there. The Rossis had an enviable, loving home life, but tonight he needed a man's counsel. He was lonely and in need of advice as he had been many times since his father had died. Outside in the beautiful wild night he found himself on the road that led to the Sutherland place. Perhaps the answer was simple. Dave would know—as steady as a rock and his loyal friend. It seemed extraordinary that he should make such a mistake in his own life. Patrice Langford rated a suicide jump in Dario's book.

CHAPTER EIGHT

FRANCES looked up at the darkening sky. It was rather frightening and exciting too, an electrical storm. She had better start on back home. She must have been walking for well over an hour. Not the best afternoon for a walk. It was far too hot and now a storm brewing, but she had been driven out of the house by a restless compulsion. Her head was still aching, but she kept walking as if she were drugged. There wasn't all that much shelter about. She would have to steer clear of the trees in case of lightning.

The beautiful countryside wore a drowsy, brooding air, very still and smouldering, waiting for the imminent storm. It would clear the air. She hoped so. For the first time since she had come to Sugar Hill there was a constraint between herself and her grandfather. Even Dario seemed edgy and out of sorts, embroiled in his own problems, yet he had worked well enough this morning to satisfy even Grandfather. The mill would stop crushing soon and the rest of the crop had to be brought in. Those great purple-black clouds moving over the great tract of farmland bewitched her. The underside of them was laced with silver like chain lightning. They seemed to be moving in slow motion—or was it she that was moving that way? She was so tired. Incredibly she had cried herself to sleep the night before and woken with a throbbing headache. Events had taken a heavy toll of her strength. She was used to a smooth life, that was it.

She longed for her mother, the sane common sense that was Chris. With any luck at all she should get a letter today. It momentarily brightened her. She hadn't realised she had made such a long trek. The outward journey had flown under her feet, absorbed as she had been in her own intense thoughts and speculations. She had worn herself out with the demands of her own passionate nature. She would simply have to sit for a moment. If the worst came to the worst, she could take shelter at the Madigan place. The Old Haunt, the local children called it, a deserted farmhouse. It was a good quarter of a mile off, but she could see its red, corrugated iron roof.

The rising wind lifted the coils of her hair. It swung madly about her small, flushed face. I hate myself, she said soundlessly. And why do you hate yourself? her other self said. Because I've allowed myself to fall in love with the wrong man—an age-old dilemma. Her sensitive mouth quivered in distress. What went on behind those silvery eyes, so clear and transparent she had been tricked into thinking she had seen some tenderness there, some flame of attraction? What did she really know about men and their infinite capacity for affairs? He had seen so much of life. There was some indefinable thing about him, a combination of qualities, a knowledge and awareness, an innate sophistication, a background of breeding and position. Why couldn't she have picked on an ordinary type? A schoolteacher? Even Dario was too clever for her.

Women were the faithful ones. Take Madellana. She had loved Dario since the first grade. If she was to be believed at all, it was Madellana and not the teacher who had taught Dario the intricacies of the alphabet and which bat went with what ball. Frances swallowed on a dry throat. She was longing

177

for a glass of water. All sorts of things had happened to her since she had come to Sugar Hill and now this. The thought of her formidable inheritance paled into insignificance beside the emotion that gripped her every time she thought of David Sutherland. She could feel the heat mount to the head. She had been using Dario's name as if it were a magic wand to keep him off. She had known all along she could never marry her cousin. Her feeling for Dario was very genuine, her pride in him great, but she did not love him in the passionate possessive way a woman reserved for her life's mate.

She felt as if in some strange way she was going to pieces. Would it pass? It had to. She couldn't seem to concentrate on anything else. She would have to do something quick. Anything. Go home to Auckland. Forget Sugar Hill, though she would never regret the experience. Dario would marry his Madellana and she knew in her heart the marriage would work. Physical love didn't always keep people together. Understanding and companionship, a similar view of life was important. Her young face was tormented, touched by a melancholy resignation. She sat by the side of the road, her elbows on her knees and her face hidden by the massy swing of her hair. Every step had cost her an effort. Never had the end of the road loomed so distinctly far off.

A moment later, a terrific clap of thunder brought her to her feet with the frightened spring of a young animal. Running along the dusty red track, head down, it amused her just how quickly she had jumped. She hadn't realised before that just how unhappy she was. Another fork of lightning rent the clouds and she put her head down to run in earnest. Any moment the rain would come down and she wouldn't make shelter. Her legs were trembling. How silly! She had worn herself out with her emotional outburst the night before. She hadn't cried herself to sleep for years.

David, oh, David!

She kept running, her heart beating frantically inside her like the heart of a trapped small bird. *David!* ... This terrible longing had to pass. It was too uncomfortable, for one thing, and it was slowing her down.

From the top of the hill Sutherland spotted her running, full pelt along the track, skidding a bit on the loose stones. Dull bronze sunlight struck across his face showing the metallic flash of his eyes. One lean hard hand pulled on the reins bringing the stallion's head up. It was reefing a little in adverse reaction to the peculiar climatic conditions, the livid sky, the rising wind, the agonised screech of birds, circling with a great spread of wings. Did she ever consider the effect of her actions? Quietening the big, reefing animal, he set it down the steep incline, a muscle jerking beside his taut mouth. What she really deserved was a thrashing. A two-year-old child would have more sense than to wander about aimlessly with a hailstorm threatening. It didn't occur to him to question his own disproportionate pitch of fury. He only wanted to shake her hard so her head lolled helplessly on that flower neck.

For once he wished he had horse power beneath him instead of this beautiful, nervous animal. His fear was of the hail. It could be deadly to all three of them, man, woman, and his highly strung thoroughbred, but there was no time now. He had to go on. With any luck they could reach the Madigan place before all hell broke loose. He had seen conditions like these before in the tropical parts of the world and they bothered him. Hail would bring havoc to these parts. Down on the flat he put the stallion to the gallop.

Relief and panic was mingled in her eyes and her voice. 'David!'

He swung down in the saddle getting a grip on her arm, forcing himself to speak in a level tone. 'Get up here. No one but you would choose this afternoon to go walk about.' His tone was all her nerves needed. She was in front of him, his arm encircling her slender rib cage, deliberately crushing her, she thought, but she didn't mind in the least. Her legs wouldn't have carried her another foot. With every flash of lightning, every drum roll of thunder the black stallion seemed on the point of acting up, but true to its breed, it flew over the soft scented canegrass with its long powerful drive shaft, the tight sensitive skin showing the sinewy sculpturing of muscle, the petite ears pricked back with the wind.

The peace and quiet of the countryside was exploding about them. Birds and small animals were racing for cover, flocks of screeching birds planing in for the trees. A minute more the rain was suspended, then it came down, and with it the hail, just as he feard. Hail that was to devastate an area of five square miles and miraculously miss the stud and his precious animals. Trees, farm buildings, power lines, stock and crops were to be damaged. The young ratoons in the canefields, Sugar Hill's standover fields. Crops bruised by the force of the lethal hail, pitted and torn, leaves shredded and stalks defoliated, giving the once beautiful fields an appearance of annihilation. It was later necessary to start running fires to prevent an outbreak of disease in the damaged crops.

Frances, crushed up against the man's lean frame, was amazed how little fear she felt in the midst of elemental fury. A steel claw of lightning smote an old paper bark and brought it crashing to the ground in a mass of flying bracken, stunning and killing the bird life that had taken shelter in it.

'Keep your head down,' he blazed near her ear. 'Do what I tell you.'

'I'm sorry, I'm sorry,' she was murmuring to herself, unaware that she had her face upflung to the wind and the storm.

He bent over her, feeling the fiery raw cut in his back. A jagged chunk of ice had hit him there, piercing the skin. A few more solid chunks had hit his nape and pounded his back and unprotected head. He gave the stallion the order and it obeyed, gathering itself and lifting its slender powerful legs to fly over the high wooden rail that surrounded the Madigan place.

'My beauty! my beauty!' The man ran his hand down the black satin arch of neck. The stallion had come down on a single forefoot and thundered on without a break, a wonderful combination of flat runner and jumper. It went on inside the old stable without even a nervous glance about the strange musty place. Sutherland dismounted, wiping the rain from his face and his shining black head. He put up his hand and Frances slipped down into his grasp, resting for a moment against the stallion's sleek back feeling the warm, shifting muscle. She was breathless, keyed up, trembling but trying to smile.

'It's all so violent!'

'Yes.'

Scot turned away from her abruptly, speaking to the stallion, calming it, while it flicked its ears back to him, listening, its nostrils blown wide, huffing at its master and friend. He seemed intent on the stallion, looking about for something to wipe it down, so Frances crossed the dusty floor shutting what was left of the stable door. The upper half was gone, but the lower creaked rustily on its hinges but held, blocking out most of the wind and the pelting hail the size of a man's fist.

'There's blood on your shirt!' she said, her voice jumpy.

'Forget about it!' he said over his shoulder, in a very preoccupied tone that still didn't fool her.

'Are you angry with me, David?'

'Yes, but I should be used to you by now.' For him, the tone was colourless as if he was holding himself back.

Flashes of lightning were all about them. Frances turned back to the storm. Because he had protected her, her hair and most of her shirt was only damp. Her slacks and sandals hadn't fared so well, but she didn't care. The rain on her face was wonderfully pure. She could taste it in her mouth. Her hair, affected by the damp, was clinging and curling on to her face like a small child's. She moistened her mouth nervously, staring out at the storm, her amber eyes clear as the rain. It was a bitter joy to be here with him while the tempest raged outside. A bird, that had taken shelter in the high beams, cried mournfully and she jerked about in a panic.

'Oh, that frightened me!'

'Pull yourself together,' he said, rather tersely. 'I'm not angry with you any more and everything's all right. How you wear yourself out.'

He walked towards her, thrusting the tendrils of curls away from her face. His eyes were brilliant, glittering strangely in his taut, dark face. He put out his hands and gripped her upper arms leaving bruises on her soft flesh. She was trembling uncontrollably at the hard disturbing look on his face. He looked like a man possessed of some daemon. She brushed her hand across her forehead as if it was some kind of incantation to ward him off. Always the same face, she thought. The same face, The same voice. It would always be like that for her. She had become a prisoner enmeshed in her own desire, the force of which was drawing him to her.

His glance covered her, her face, her mouth, her soft, creamy throat, so that she looked heartbreakingly moody and wretched. 'Don't look at me like that, David. You're making me nervous. Say something!'

'Like what?' he asked, in a hard, humorous tone. 'The atmosphere is hardly conducive to idle chatter. At the same time, this extravagance, this thunder and lightning is the emotional climate you need.'

The realisation that this was male aggression came to her. 'Why are you attacking me?'

There was a suspicion of self-contempt in his eyes. 'Maybe I *have* to! In some ways we're well matched.'

Her amber eyes went past him, searching out the gloomy corners of the barn. 'Lovers and fugitives usually hide out in deserted farmhouses. Which are we?'

'I'm not entirely sure,' he said, turning her face back to him with the force of one long finger. 'It did seem to me you were becoming forgetful of your surroundings, Frances. You're ravishing with the rain on your face and your hair curling in the heat. A delicious *jeune fille*, a long-stemmed rose. It's also pretty damned clear you're forbiddingly innocent. Ally that to a sweet, passionate nature and that's trouble for any man.'

'Are you frightened?' she asked, surprised that she could meet those shimmering eyes at all.

'I am! I'm not too proud to admit it.'

'What an admission for the great David Sutherland!' she retorted too smartly, a flame-coloured curl falling on to her forehead. The hail on the roof might well have been the cooing of doves for all the notice she took of it.

'What is it you want, Frances?' he asked in a hard undertone.

'Make love to me!' she said, momentarily thrown right off balance. She wanted him to so much he must feel it.

'No!' he said, emphatically heartless.

'Why not?' she asked, roused to a reckless passion.

'I might do it more thoroughly than you want. I'm certainly capable of it.'

'You're *that*!' she hurled at him in a frenzy of rejection, her delicate face flushed with the force of her emotions. 'I've come so far to meet you—a long journey. Love is a journey. It's not always easy and it's not even pleasant, and for me there's no guarantee of a safe return.'

Taut pressure lines formed beside his chiselled mouth, tension in every line of him. 'Are you trying to tell me you love me?'

'I'm telling you *nothing*!' she declared, like the outbreak of war.

'Say it. Say you love me!'

'I won't. It's only desire I feel.'

'If it's only that, then I can match it!' he said, catching her soft shoulder.

'I've found some chink in that invincible armour, haven't I?' she challenged him, looking full into his splintering eyes.

'You have.'

'I'm glad!' She said it, but her eyelashes fell before the expression on his dark, handsome face. Hard masculine desire and no mirror to his heart.

'Let's see how good you are when you can't talk!' He looked down at her still, triangular face, then swept her into his arms unable to subdue his own emotions, taking no account of her slender fragility or the certain knowledge that he was hurting her. He wanted to. If he expected to find resistance, she offered none. Her ardent young mouth parted and she clung to him, totally committed, whatever the outcome. That was her nature and there was no escape from him.

Finding so little will to oppose him, the ruthless pressure of his mouth eased and the hand that held her head fast gently tugged on her curls, tilting her face more fully back to him. Her heart was shattering, shattering, and still the rain came down and the wild wind blew across the land.

Nowadays when the wind blew Frances found herself possessed of a brittle energy that made her turn her hand to anything—gardening, sailing, swimming, a course of home dressmaking. Nothing helped. Her mother worried about her and even Chris looked long and hard at this fantastic little creature he called his daughter. The trip to Queensland had done all this, altered her. Of course it was a shock, the death of her grandfather and the damage to the property Sugar Hill, but that was all over. Vincent Donovan had been two months short of his eighty-fifth year—a good innings. Unlikely I shall reach it, Chris thought. He stopped at the traffic lights and glanced sideways at Frances' tense little face. Used as he had become to countless fireworks since her childhood, he realised she was bottling up some strong emotion within her, but whatever it was she wasn't yet ready to speak about it. It wasn't her cousin, young Dario, because she had just had a letter from him which she read out to them over dinner without missing a line and with something of her old vitality. Dario was making a study tour of Europe and taking his mother. The farm had been sold up. It was Dario's intention to call on them when the boat called in at Auckland. So everything was all right there! Ah well, young people, Chris thought, they had to work out their own problems, get a hold on their own destiny. The only fortunate part was, as Rae said to him last night, Frances was one of those girls whose looks seemed to improve with heartache. Glancing at her briefly again as the lights changed he saw it was true. She was a lovely girl, but she was no longer a child and she was weeping gems for someone. Who?

Coming down the drive in the soft twilight they could see the lamps burning, one at the top of the drive, one at the base of the drive and one in the garden. Rae must have turned them all on. Probably the three at the foot of their sandstone cliff frontage were burning brightly as well. They must have visitors, Rae had probably turned them all on as a special effect, a kind of celebration. He had bought all six in London many, many years ago. They were something of a tradition around the place. Certainly many people enjoyed them and their soft brilliance. They enhanced the scene.

Frances, all of a sudden, seemed to come out of her reverie. She sat forward, her heart pounding. 'Mummy must have found someone important!' The first shock waves were hitting her. She had no control over them. Chris had lost his frail claim on her attention. Rae had come out on to the front porch, waving. She wore a long hostess dress, one of his favourites. Important indeed! A tall man followed her. Youngish, about thirty-five. Even at that distance he had considerable presence. Damned good-looking too. Chris didn't steer the car into the garage but pulled up in the drive, feeling the seething restlessness in his stepdaughter, the gathering excitement. He turned his head, making a vain attempt to open the car door for her, but she was already out, moving in her flying leaf fashion, her footsteps noiseless, her face so profoundly young and lovely, so vivid with life that he, a man in his fifties, felt the tears start to his eyes. He wouldn't be young again for anything. The pleasure and the pain. What agony was young love!

Under the pear tree she went calling with her heart in her voice, like a nightingale singing: 'David!'

So there it was! Chris thought. The answer to the impenetrable mystery. *David*. With a faintly wry smile on his face, his hand oustretched, Chris went up the stairs to meet this man who was to become so much a part of them all. David Sutherland. The man met him half way. One look was enough to tell Chris all he wanted to know, their own little Frances was safe. At the centre of her heart, out of the vastness of her own country she had found a rock hard shoulder to lean on, a man they could trust with all their hearts.

'Did you think you were seeing ghosts?' Sutherland asked, catching Frances' slender hand, kissing the fingertips and drawing her to him.

She smiled up at him, searching his dear, dark, familiar face, the radiance of her smile almost stopping the breath in his throat, making all the long days, week after week, seem worth while. She had to know her own mind. It was important to him. She was so young! He had to give her time.

'I always knew you'd turn up!' she said audaciously, teasing him, the heartache over and forgotten.

He smiled at her, silver eyes brilliant. His own obsessive young love. Frances.

F R E E ! ! !

Did you know.....?

that just by mailing in the coupon below you can receive a brand new, up-to-date "Harlequin Romance Catalogue" listing literally hundreds of Harlequin Romances you probably thought were out of print.

Now you can shop in your own home for novels by your favorite Harlequin authors — the Essie Summers you wanted to read, the Violet Winspear you missed, the Mary Burchell you thought wasn't available anymore!

They're all listed in the "Harlequin Romance Catalogue". And something else too — the books are listed in numerical sequence, — so you can fill in the missing numbers in your library.

Don't delay — mail the coupon below to us today. We'll promptly send you the "Harlequin Romance Catalogue".

PLEASE NOTE: Harlequin Romance Catalogue of available titles is revised every three months.

FREE!

TO: **HARLEQUIN READER SERVICE, Dept. N 507**
M.P.O. Box 707, Niagara Falls, N.Y. 14302
Canadian address: Stratford, Ont., Canada

☐ Please send me the free Harlequin Romance Catalogue.
☐ Please send me the titles checked.

I enclose $_____ (No C.O.D.'s). All books listed are 60c each. To help defray postage and handling cost, please add 25c.

Name _____

Address _____

City/Town _____

State/Prov. _____ Zip _____

Have You Missed Any of Thes.
Harlequin Romances?

PLEASE NOTE: All Harlequin Romances from #1857 onwards are 75c. Books below that number, **where available** are priced at 60c through Harlequin Reader Service until December 31st, 1975.

AA

Have You Missed Any of These
Harlequin Romances?

- ☐ 941 MAYENGA FARM
  Kathryn Blair
- ☐ 945 DOCTOR SANDY
  Margaret Malcolm
- ☐ 948 ISLANDS OF SUMMER
  Anne Weale
- ☐ 951 THE ENCHANTED TRAP
  Kate Starr
- ☐ 957 NO LEGACY FOR LINDSAY
  Essie Summers
- ☐ 965 CAME A STRANGER
  Celine Conway
- ☐ 968 SWEET BRENDA
  Penelope Walsh
- ☐ 974 NIGHT OF THE HURRICANE
  Andrea Blake
- ☐ 984 ISLAND IN THE DAWN
  Averil Ives
- ☐ 993 SEND FOR NURSE ALISON
  Marjorie Norrell
- ☐ 994 JUBILEE HOSPITAL
  Jan Tempest
- ☐ 1001 NO PLACE FOR SURGEONS
  Elizabeth Gilzean
- ☐ 1004 THE PATH OF THE
  MOONFISH, Betty Beaty
- ☐ 1009 NURSE AT FAIRCHILDS
  Marjorie Norrell
- ☐ 1010 DOCTOR OF RESEARCH
  Elizabeth Houghton
- ☐ 1011 THE TURQUOISE SEA
  Hilary Wilde
- ☐ 1018 HOSPITAL IN THE TROPICS
  Gladys Fullbrook
- ☐ 1019 FLOWER OF THE MORNING
  Celine Conway
- ☐ 1024 THE HOUSE OF DISCONTENT
  Esther Wyndham
- ☐ 1048 HIGH MASTER OF CLERE
  Jane Arbor
- ☐ 1052 MEANT FOR EACH OTHER
  Mary Burchell
- ☐ 1074 NEW SURGEON AT ST.
  LUCIAN'S, Elizabeth
  Houghton
- ☐ 1087 A HOME FOR JOCELYN
  Eleanor Farnes
- ☐ 1094 MY DARK RAPPAREE
  Henrietta Reid

- ☐ 1098 THE UNCHARTED OCEAN
  Margaret Malcolm
- ☐ 1102 A QUALITY OF MAGIC
  Rose Burghely
- ☐ 1106 WELCOME TO PARADISE
  Jill Tahourdin
- ☐ 1115 THE ROMANTIC HEART
  Norrey Ford
- ☐ 1120 HEART IN HAND
  Margaret Malcolm
- ☐ 1121 TEAM DOCTOR, Ann Gilmour
- ☐ 1122 WHISTLE AND I'LL COME
  Flora Kidd
- ☐ 1138 LOVING IS GIVING
  Mary Burchell
- ☐ 1144 THE TRUANT BRIDE
  Sara Seale
- ☐ 1150 THE BRIDE OF MINGALAY
  Jean S. Macleod
- ☐ 1166 DOLAN OF SUGAR HILLS
  Kate Starr
- ☐ 1172 LET LOVE ABIDE
  Norrey Ford
- ☐ 1182 GOLDEN APPLE ISLAND
  Jane Arbor
- ☐ 1183 NEVER CALL IT LOVING
  Marjorie Lewty
- ☐ 1184 THE HOUSE OF OLIVER
  Jean S. Macleod
- ☐ 1200 SATIN FOR THE BRIDE
  Kate Starr
- ☐ 1201 THE ROMANTIC DR. RYDON
  Anne Durham
- ☐ 1209 THE STUBBORN DR STEPHEN
  Elizabeth Houghton
- ☐ 1211 BRIDE OF KYLSAIG
  Iris Danbury
- ☐ 1214 THE MARSHALL FAMILY
  Mary Burchell
- ☐ 1216 ORANGES AND LEMONS
  Isobel Chace
- ☐ 1218 BEGGARS MAY SING
  Sara Seale
- ☐ 1222 DARK CONFESSOR
  Elinor Davis
- ☐ 1236 JEMIMA
  Leonora Starr

PLEASE NOTE: All Harlequin Romances from #1857 onwards are 75c. Books below that number, **where available** are priced at 60c through Harlequin Reader Service until December 31st, 1975.

BB

Have You Missed Any of These

Harlequin Romances?

PLEASE NOTE: All Harlequin Romances from #1857 onwards are 75c. Books below that number, where available are priced at 60c through Harlequin Reader Service until December 31st, 1975.